UNMASKED:
THE SCIENCE OF SUPERHEROES

R. WALSH, S. ROBINSON, N. DANINO, C. TENNICK, S. ANSCOMBE, M. DICKINSON, A. WILCOX

CONTENTS

CONTENTS

SUPERHUMAN BODIES

CATHERINE is a Senior Lecturer in Forensic Science at the University of Central Lancashire, England. Catherine (also known as Cat) is a Forensic Scientist and loves having the same job title as Barry Allen a.k.a. The Flash. She also enjoys running (but definitely not at Flash speeds!) She investigates evidence that might be found at crime scenes, to pinpoint what something may be and what it may say about the case at hand. When Cat isn't experimenting in the lab, she loves experimenting with ingredients in the kitchen to make themed cakes, learning to play lots of musical instruments and following her curiosity wherever a new adventure takes her!

INTRODUCTION

Superheroes have amazing qualities that allow them to perform incredible feats; their skills often viewed as far superior to the abilities of an ordinary human being. Super strength, endurance and healing powers are just a few examples of superhuman abilities that provide the means for gripping adventures.

This chapter looks at some of the skills that characters like Superman or Captain Marvel possess, and question if superhumans could actually exist outside of a comic book or film franchise. Are those stories just tales to thrill an audience, or is there any basis in reality? Could anyone ever become a superhuman?

SUPERHERO ORIGINS: WHERE DID IT ALL BEGIN?

As you watch superhero blockbusters, like *Black Panther* or *Avengers: Endgame*, it is easy to imagine that the concept of superhumans is a modern phenomenon. Almost two thousand years ago, philosopher Lucian of Samosata (born 125 AD and died after 180 AD) is said to be the earliest science fiction writer in Western civilisation. He wrote *A True Story*, covering voyages in space, extra-terrestrial life and interplanetary warfare. In another of his works, he talked about something called **hyperanthropos**, meaning 'more than man' in Greek; but how did an Ancient Greek philosopher inspire a modern-day phenomenon?

In 1883, German philosopher Friedrich Nietzsche had ideas based on Lucian's work and began to think about human beings overcoming their own restrictions, suggesting that when they did, they would become better for it. He named the person who would do this someday a 'superman' or 'beyond-man' ('übermensch' in German). He thought that people with these 'superman'

FRIEDRICH NIETZSCHE

qualities would be stronger than normal humans and not restricted by other people's ideas of right and wrong. Nietzsche's ideas inspired the writers of *The Reign of the Superman* comic story in 1933.

The title character of this story is a telepathic villain, rather than a physically powerful hero like the character we are familiar with today. It wasn't until 18th April 1938 when Superman — as we know him — was finally published in the first issue of *Action Comics*, holding a car high above his head!

So now we know the origins of super strength, how could we build our own strength? And could it be like that of Superman or other superheroes?

Physical strength, in simple terms, is the measure of one's exertion of force on an object. It is undoubtedly one of the most common traits of being a superhero, with heroes such as the Hulk, Captain Marvel, Spider-Man and Wonder Woman lifting objects far heavier than any normal human could. However, there are documented examples of 'ordinary' people demonstrating extraordinary feats of strength. In July 2017, Kevin Fast pulled a 99,060 kilogram fire engine over 100 feet (the weight equivalent of fourteen bull elephants) and in 2013, Lisa Griminas pulled a 7,711 kilogram transport truck 100 feet — the equivalent of one bull elephant. These are spectacular displays of strength, but how do they compare to superhumans? In *Captain America: Civil War*, Cap manages to hold a helicopter from taking off that weighs an estimated 3,000 pounds (1.36 tonnes) and Hulk holds the weight of a 150 billion tonne mountain during the *Secret Wars* comic. That's some serious power! So, how could it be done?

HOW DO MUSCLES WORK?

The building blocks of strength come from the structure of the human body. Your body is made of lots of tiny structures called cells, each with a different job to do. Cells are like biological building blocks, which have different shapes and are structured to do different things. Cells work together to become your bones and muscles, and all have a part to play in lifting a substantial weight.

Muscles like **biceps** (arms), **pectorals** (chest) and the **quadriceps** (legs) are known as skeletal muscles because they attach to the skeleton to generate movement. They are also responsible for maintaining our posture, stabilising joints and generating heat. They work in pairs — when one muscle in a pair relaxes, the other contracts. This is because skeletal muscles can only pull in one direction, so pairs allow muscles to pull in several directions. Muscle cells are made of **proteins**, long and complicated chemical chains that are essential to the human body, making up structures like muscles and hair, as well as playing a role in how we digest our food (**enzymes**) and the ways in which we protect our bodies from germs (**antibodies**).

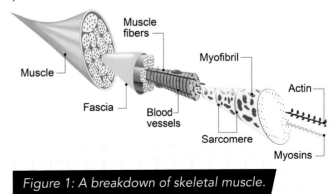

Figure 1: A breakdown of skeletal muscle.

Figure 2: An example of a deadlift.

Our muscle proteins include **actin** and **myosin**, string-like proteins that form muscle **filaments**. These filament cells slide past each other, making muscles contract and relax, changing the length and shape of the cell, causing movement of the muscle.

The image above shows an example of **deadlifting** and what occurs to the body during the lift. It may look simple, but there are a number of complicated things happening within the lifter's body. When you lift in this manner, a nervous impulse from the brain travels to nerves at the skeletal muscles like the **hamstring** (muscle behind the thigh), releasing a chemical which causes the muscle to contract, pulling the lower leg upwards and causing the knees to bend. The **quadriceps** (at the front of your thigh) then relaxes. To return to standing position, the quadriceps contract and the hamstring relaxes, straightening the legs and the knee joint. You can bend your hamstring and your quadriceps by trying out a Spider-Man style crouch. As you bend and stand — which muscles are contracting and relaxing? The diagram to the right should help you.

You can also try this with your arm muscles, like Superman getting ready to lift a car in his first adventure! Hold your arm out straight in front of you and bend your arm at the elbow (like you want to show off your muscles!) The **biceps** muscle in your upper arm contracts, pulling your forearm towards your shoulder. This is known as **flexion**. Your biceps cannot straighten your arm again, so if you want to straighten your arm, a different muscle carrying out the opposite action, the triceps (the muscle underneath your upper arm) pulls it straight to extend the arm once again.

HOW DO YOU BUILD MUSCLES WITHOUT BEING EXPOSED TO GAMMA RADIATION OR SPIDER BITES?

To grow, muscles need to be exercised regularly and rested appropriately, as well as ensuring that you eat enough protein as part of a balanced diet. Growth of muscle cells is known as **hypertrophy** and this is helped if you eat correctly, and why characters like The Flash must eat large amounts of food after exerting their muscles. Sources of protein include lean meats, chicken, fish, eggs, beans, milk, yoghurt and pulses (a type of dried seed). Muscles after exercise break down and begin to rebuild. This is why nutrition is important, and rest periods between exercise are vital for muscle repair and growth.

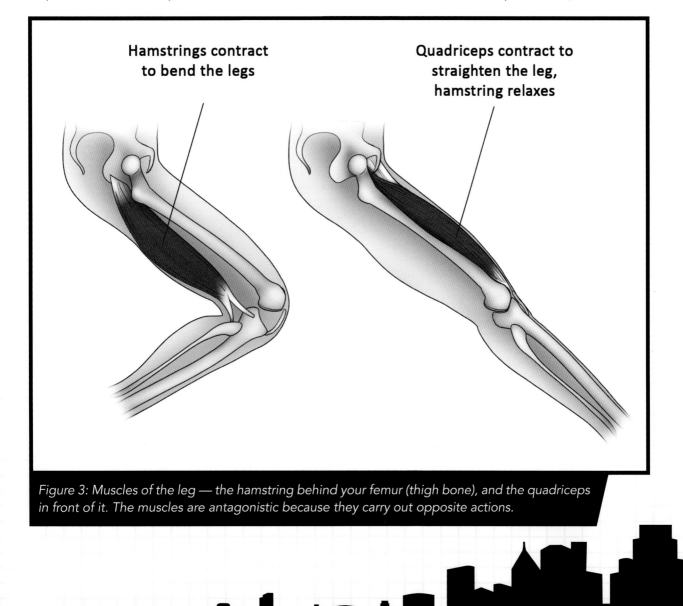

Hamstrings contract to bend the legs

Quadriceps contract to straighten the leg, hamstring relaxes

Figure 3: Muscles of the leg — the hamstring behind your femur (thigh bone), and the quadriceps in front of it. The muscles are antagonistic because they carry out opposite actions.

Muscle size increases most by resistance exercises, which means using our muscles to lift a heavy load (like the barbell our earlier deadlifter used). This forces the muscles to contract as hard as they can, stressing the muscles and increasing the number of filaments within your muscle cells. The muscles then undergo **hypertrophy** (cells get bigger) and therefore you get bigger muscles! All types of exercise will increase the number of muscle proteins, such as **myoglobin proteins**, which store oxygen for the muscles, ready for when it is needed.

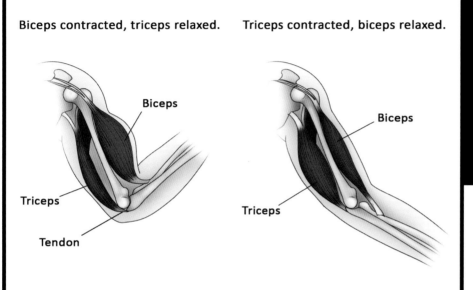

Biceps contracted, triceps relaxed.

Triceps contracted, biceps relaxed.

Biceps

Biceps

Triceps

Triceps

Tendon

Figure 4: Antagonistic muscle pairs — your bicep and tricep would be used if you wanted to bend your arm, for example, to lift a heavy weight. The bicep contracts, lifting the arm towards the upper body. The tricep contracts to release and straighten the arm.

Bigger muscle cells need more energy, and cells have their own power stations inside them known as **mitochondria** (often known as the powerhouses in the cell). They act a bit like the digestive system of the cell, taking in nutrients and breaking them down, creating a rich source of energy for them to keep up the action, whether it's preparing muscles for running like The Flash or leaping from building to building like Spider-Man.

Lots of mitochondria mean that muscles can also produce and use more energy to lift heavier weights, or run faster and further for longer.

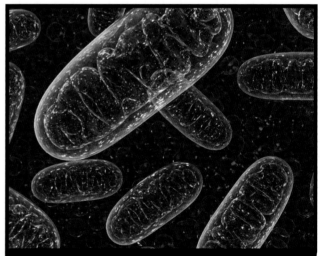

Figure 5: It looks like a wrinkly jelly bean — but these are mitochondria. Muscle cells have many mitochondria, whereas nerve cells have very few.

ARE BIGGER MUSCLES BETTER?

We now know how to make our muscles bigger, but are larger muscles necessarily stronger? In 2015, researchers looked at microscopic muscle fibres from bodybuilders, athletes and non-athletes. They looked at the size of muscles and the speed of which cells contracted to calculate the specific force for a defined unit of muscle. The higher the force, the better the quality of muscle. Although the bodybuilder muscle fibres were bigger than those in the non-athletes, they had a lower specific force. The athletes had similar quality muscles to the non-athletes but could produce force faster, indicating that their muscles were more powerful than the larger muscles of the bodybuilders!

Bigger muscles can be an indication of strength, but this study demonstrates that smaller muscles can produce more force than big muscles, meaning that there may be an optimum size for muscles, over which you no longer get an equal return of additional strength.

BECOMING 'SUPERHUMAN' – MAKING THE MOST OF MUSCLES

Skeletal muscle contains two types of muscle, known as **Type One (slow twitch)** and **Type Two (fast twitch)**. They each serve different purposes — Type Two muscles can help us to run quickly away from an enemy, for example, whereas Type One muscles would help you to carry on running for miles without stopping to find help.

Type One muscles contain many capillaries, as well as lots of power-providing mitochondria and the oxygen-carrying protein myoglobin (which we talked about earlier) to help muscles move. Myoglobin also gives muscle its characteristic red colour!

Type One fibres can contract for long periods of time, but with very little force. These muscles are often associated with posture, and marathon athletes like David Weir or Paula Radcliffe build high numbers of these fibres through training as they are useful for endurance sports.

Type Two muscles contract with rapidity and power but tire very quickly and consume lots of energy. Think about how tired you feel after sprinting to catch the bus or the train! They are most useful for sprint athletes like Kadeena Cox or Usain

Figure 6: Different muscle types are better suited for particular activities. Type One muscles are better for endurance and distance sports like marathon running. . .

Figure 7: . . . whereas Type Two muscles are better for short bursts of power, such as sprinting.

Bolt because they allow short **anaerobic** (without oxygen) bursts of activity before the contraction of the muscles becomes painful. Type Two muscles contribute to the overall strength of the muscle and have the greatest potential for an increase in size.

In order to stimulate Type Two muscles and gain overall strength, heavy weights are needed, as lifting small weights will only stimulate smaller muscles.

Heavier weights means fewer repetitions of the lift are possible; in fact, the International Sports Science Association suggests that lifting a weight more than six times in a row probably means it is no longer activating your Type Two muscles.

Repetitions with heavier weights need to be gradually increased, which comes with practice. It is also suggested that a short period of rest is effective because it naturally raises the level of **human growth hormone (HGH)** in your body and therefore assists in increasing muscle size.

So we now know that you can make your muscles bigger and stronger, and it is possible for humans to demonstrate feats of super strength, helped by regular training, exercise, rest and a balanced diet. But what about gaining strength, speed and other abilities from external substances, such as a super formula?

In the Marvel comics, Black Widow and Captain America received versions of something known as the super soldier serum, enhancing their human bodily functions to peak efficiency. Spider-Man villain Green Goblin gained powers through a scientific formula, and Batman's enemy Bane gained super strength after he was tested with a substance known as venom (not to be confused with Spider-Man's foe). The super-formula in each case aided strength and endurance, but could these kinds of serums actually exist? The answer may lie in chemicals already inside our body and brain.

We've talked about how muscle strength can be affected by diet and exercise, but the size of our muscles can also be influenced by chemicals naturally produced in the body known as hormones, namely HGH. HGH is produced by the **pituitary gland** in the brain and starts the growth spurts we see in children and adolescents. For the rest of us, it also has roles in protein production (vital for muscle growth), encouraging fat use by the body and maintaining blood sugar (glucose) levels at set amounts.

In 1985, synthetic HGH was manufactured and promoted for weight loss because it can prevent carbohydrates from being turned into fats. Adverts suggested it sped up your metabolism, built muscle, and contained anti-ageing properties.

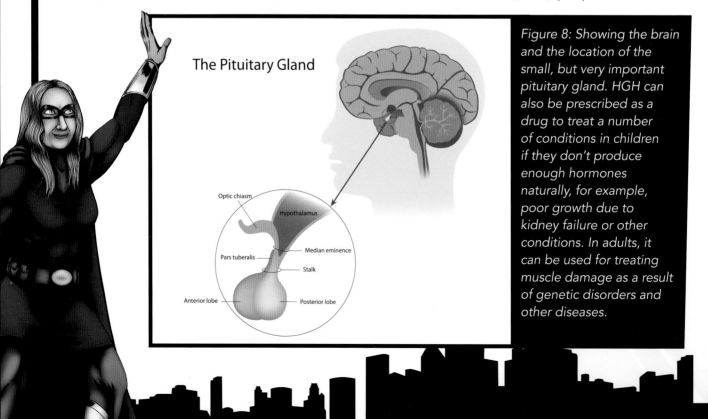

The Pituitary Gland

Optic chiasm
Hypothalamus
Median eminence
Pars tuberalis
Stalk
Anterior lobe
Posterior lobe

Figure 8: Showing the brain and the location of the small, but very important pituitary gland. HGH can also be prescribed as a drug to treat a number of conditions in children if they don't produce enough hormones naturally, for example, poor growth due to kidney failure or other conditions. In adults, it can be used for treating muscle damage as a result of genetic disorders and other diseases.

This created an online market for the drug, aimed at those looking to lose weight or increase muscle. As with any drug, taking HGH without medical supervision has risks. Reported side effects include diabetes, carpal tunnel syndrome, fluid retention, joint and muscle pain, breast enlargement and high blood pressure (which can put you at risk of heart attacks or a stroke). Other research indicates an increased risk of cancer, prostate cancer in particular. Because of this, it is illegal in the UK to possess and take this drug unless medically advised, and it is banned by sporting organisations such as the International Olympic Committee and the World Anti-Doping Agency.

Harvard Medical School conducted a review of HGH studies for treatment in healthy older people, with 220 participants receiving HGH and 227 subjects not receiving HGH. Individuals who were given the drug gained an average of 4.6 pounds (nearly 3 kilograms) of muscle and shed the same amount of fat. However, many of the side effects above were reported by participants in the study.

Researchers in California looked at 44 studies of HGH in athletes. Those taking part had an average age of 27, were physically fit and mostly male. 303 participants took HGH, and 137 received a **placebo** (a substance given that is not intended to have any value or effect on the people involved). Daily injections were given for 20 days, and — just like the previous example — HGH subjects increased their muscle mass by an average of 4.6 pounds. Despite the large gain in mass, there was no indication of improved performance for the athletes. No measurable increases in strength or exercise capacity were recorded, and those receiving HGH were more likely to report tiredness (fatigue) and fluid retention (excess fluids building up in the body). Excessive use of growth hormones in the body over a long period of time can even cause **acromegaly**, in which patients have a swelling of the hands and feet and altered facial features.

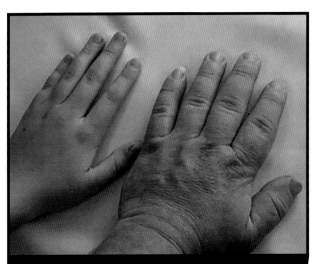

Figure 9: Someone with acromegaly in their hand (right) and someone without (left).

Another hormone which has an impact on muscles in the body is **testosterone**. Produced by the **gonads** (testes in men and ovaries in women) and the **adrenal** glands in your kidneys, testosterone increases the strength of bones and muscles in males and females. It is naturally present in much higher levels in men than women, being essential for making sperm, and responsible for many of the changes seen in boys during puberty. For women, testosterone controls the secretion of hormones linked to **menstruation** (periods) and reproduction.

Similar in structure to testosterone, **anabolic steroids** are manufactured hormones, prescribed for some types of **anaemia** (when you have low red blood cell counts) and people with unusually low hormone levels. They are not to be confused with another type of steroid commonly prescribed by doctors — **corticosteroids**, which are used to reduce swelling. Anabolic steroids are Class C drugs, meaning they can only be sold by pharmacists with a prescription.

Due to their performance-enhancing ability to increase muscle mass and reduce fat, anabolic steroids are illegal to export, import or possess if there is an intention to supply in the UK (although they are not illegal for personal use). Most professional organisations have banned anabolic steroid use and test competitors to see if they have been using them.

Similar to HGH, these drugs come with a range of physical risks including baldness, stunted growth and infertility, and can also increase the risk of heart attacks, strokes, tumours in the liver and kidney, high blood pressure and blood clots. They can also alter mood and increase levels of depression and aggression.

Those working in military environments work in difficult and challenging situations, and countries all over the world have explored ways to enhance soldier abilities. Militaries around the world have shown interest in the use of **amphetamines** to help their soldiers and pilots maintain focus and concentration over long missions. Amphetamines are drugs that speed up the body's processes including heart and breathing rate. Something that does so is known as a **stimulant**, increasing energy levels and alertness. Although amphetamines may help with wakefulness and focus, as the body's energy stores are reduced, feelings of anxiety, irritability and restlessness are commonly reported. Heavy, regular use often leads to lack of sleep and lowers resistance to disease. Delusions, panic attacks, paranoia, a feeling of being 'wired' and hallucinations may also follow, and some users even experience violent mood swings.

Performance enhancing drugs may exist to help increase strength and endurance, but currently the risks far outweigh the benefits. Therefore, the idea of a super serum is something that will very much remain in the world of comic books and movies for the foreseeable future. Using drugs to enhance performance is banned in professional sport and drugs should only ever be taken under the advice and guidance of a doctor. These substances are addictive, resulting in cravings for the drug and withdrawal symptoms if you stop taking them suddenly.

By training and exercising more regularly, you can achieve more and it is a great way to build your own level of strength and endurance. Before starting any new activity, seek out advice to make sure you increase your levels safely. If you have any questions about addiction or any of the substances mentioned in this chapter, speak to your doctor or see the resources section at the back of this book.

SUPER SUCCESS IN YOUR GENES?

So, if there is no chance of a super serum, could your **genes** be the key to superpowers? Don't raid your wardrobe for denim just yet: genes are small sections of something called **DNA (deoxyribonucleic acid)**. DNA can be found in the cells in your body and contains the instructions for living things to grow and survive. Sometimes, DNA in your genes can change, causing differences in the **organism** (living thing).

In films and comics, Professor Xavier, Rogue and Storm from the X-Men are called 'mutants'. One of their genes, known as the X-gene, gives them incredible and varied superpowers. To find out more about how this might work, we need to take a look at the structure of DNA.

DNA is made of chemicals linked together like a chain. The structure of these chains is like a ladder, but each side of the ladder has been twisted around to make a coil-like shape called a **double helix**. The sides of the ladder are made of chemicals called **phosphates** and sugars, and the rungs are made of chemicals called **bases**.

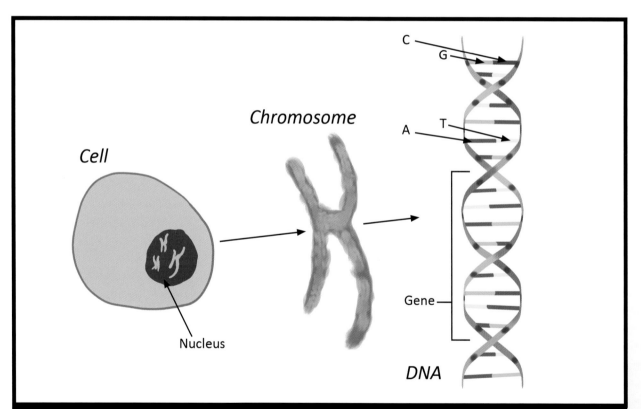

Figure 10: Diagram of the building blocks of the body. Inside the cells, DNA is wrapped up into packages called chromosomes. Unwinding the chromosomes reveals the DNA ladder (known as a double helix), containing 4 bases — A, T, C and G, which make up your genes.

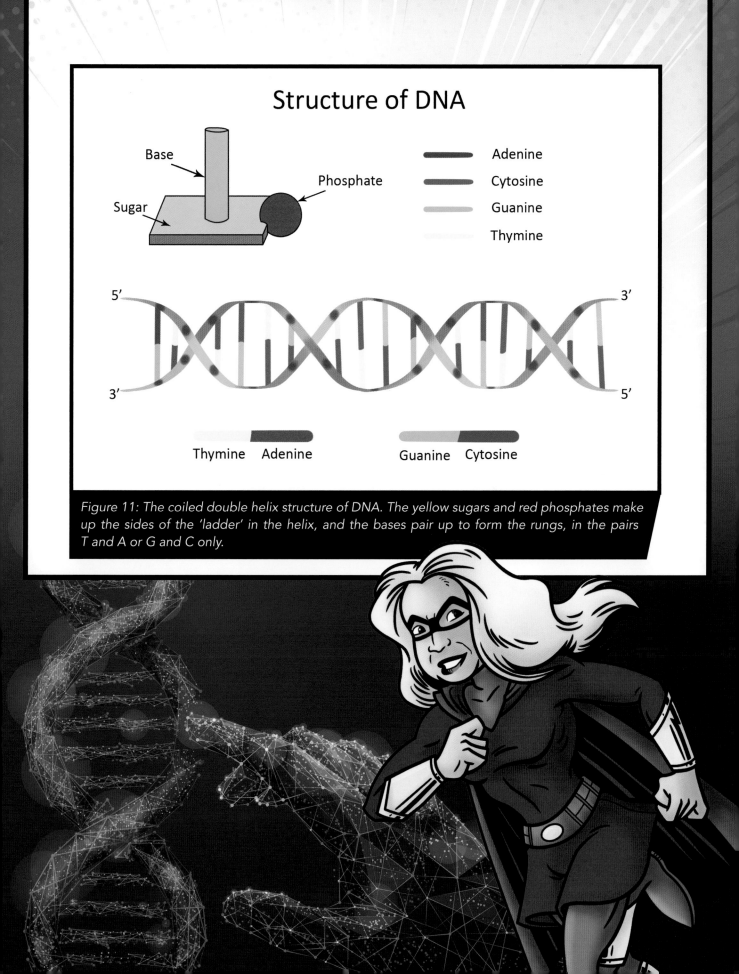

Figure 11: The coiled double helix structure of DNA. The yellow sugars and red phosphates make up the sides of the 'ladder' in the helix, and the bases pair up to form the rungs, in the pairs T and A or G and C only.

THE GENETIC 'CODE'

Bases in DNA are very important. They are called: **adenine** (A), **thymine** (T), **guanine** (G) and **cytosine** (C). Human DNA contains about three billion pairs of these bases. Think of them as ingredients in cookery that can be combined inside your DNA in different ways, like ingredients in a recipe. The many combinations of these bases are what we call **genes**, and just like how ingredients give instructions for how a recipe tastes and looks, different genes give instructions that create our characteristics, like the colour of your eyes, how tall you are, or perhaps — like in X-Men — whether or not you have superpowers! Your genes in your DNA are packed very tightly together into paired packages called **chromosomes**. In total, humans have 20,000 to 25,000 genes all contained within 23 pairs of chromosome structures. The largest chromosome contains about 8,000 genes and the smallest contains about 300.

So far, we've thought of genetic code as ingredients and recipes. However, in 2003, scientists were able to completely map out genetic instructions for human chromosomes, meaning the human genome would be around 20,000 to 25,000 recipes, each recipe representing a gene! The 'cookbook' containing all instructions for humans (and other organisms) is known as the **genome**.

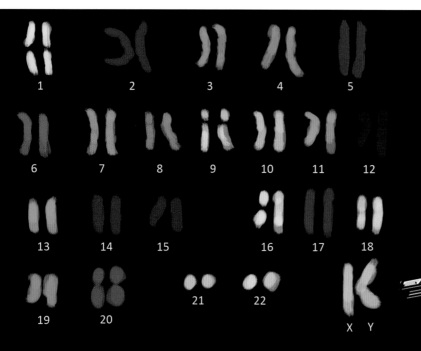

Figure 12: Microscopic image of human chromosomes. **Spectral karyotyping** is a method scientists can use to look at all chromosomes in an organism at once by 'painting' each chromosome fluorescently with a different colour.

Scientists have calculated that the difference between one human and another is less than 0.1%. In fact, we share 96% of our DNA with chimpanzees, as well as sharing common genes with fish, plants and even bacteria!

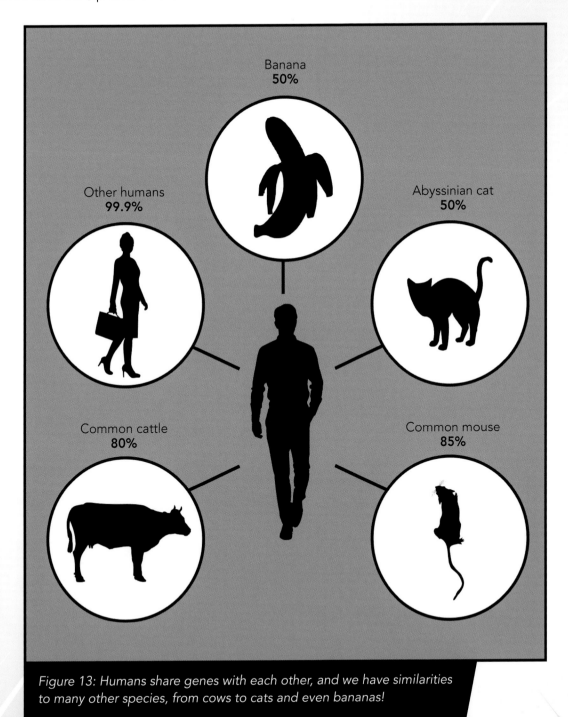

Figure 13: Humans share genes with each other, and we have similarities to many other species, from cows to cats and even bananas!

ARE MUTANTS REAL?

Shapeshifting mutants like Mystique and Nightcrawler can change the structure of their cells instantly, but for human cells to grow and survive, the cells in your body make a direct copy of the original cell; this is known as **cell division** or **mitosis**. Before cells in your body divide to make new ones, the DNA inside must be replicated to make sure the new cell is exactly the same as the old ones, including all of the genes inside it. Then each cell splits into two new cells, each getting an identical copy of the DNA. Mystique can completely change her cells to instantly take on any form, but most human cells need days or years to copy the DNA and renew the cells in them, without any significant changes to your appearance.

When first studying our cells, scientists applied something called **carbon-14 dating** (a method used to study aged fossils and historical artefacts) to look at the age of the cells in the body. They found that skin cells are renewed about every two weeks because skin is easily damaged. Bone cells renew every ten years or so, and cells taken from the eye and the brain were found to be the same age as the person they belonged to. By the time you finish reading this sentence, fifty million of your cells have died and been replaced by new ones! But on average, the cells in your body are about ten years old, so even though characters like Professor Xavier or Magneto are currently in their eighties, most of their cells might only be ten years of age (with the exception of their brains and some cells in their eyes).

MITOSIS

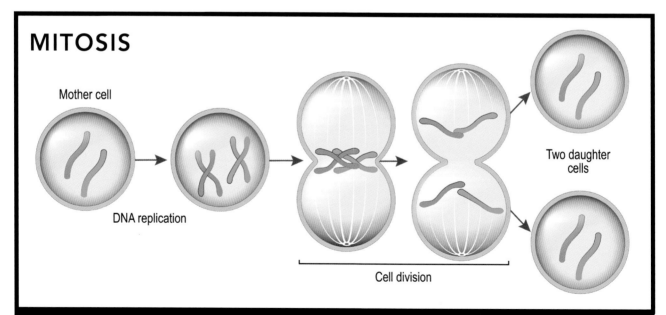

Mother cell

DNA replication

Two daughter cells

Cell division

Figure 14: Mitosis Cell Division: The original 'parent' cell copies the DNA in the chromosomes in the cell, making identical copies of DNA that are shared when the cell splits to form two new 'daughter' cells. This happens about every four months for red blood cells, which is why healthy adults can donate blood several times a year.

We've talked about the genetic 'code' in DNA and the fact that cell division by mitosis creates identical new cells with copies of the original DNA. But during the replication process, it is possible that some of the DNA may not copy correctly, from a single base (A, T, C or G) to entire sections of the chromosome. This means that our DNA can actually be changed, which we call a **mutation**. There are many different types, and some of these are shown below:

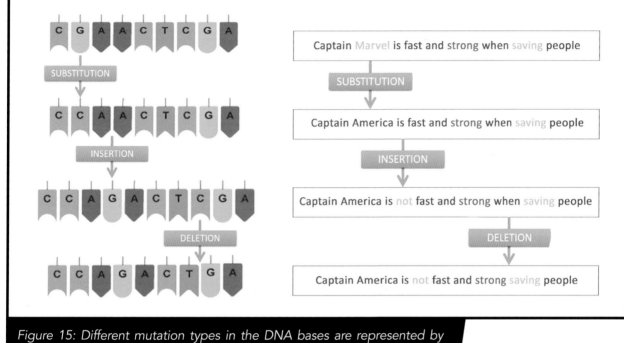

Figure 15: Different mutation types in the DNA bases are represented by changes to the sentences, with words substituted, inserted or deleted.

This is a DNA sequence, with different types of mutations — if we turn the sequence into a written sentence, you can see how each mutation might influence the way the sequence is read. Bases (A, T, C and G) can be swapped (**substitution**), added (**insertion**) and removed (**deleted**). You can see that these mutations affect the information in the sentence, which is essentially how they affect the information in your DNA.

Mutations could benefit you and possibly make your life better, but they can also have a negative effect. Many of us will walk around with mutations that we may never notice because they have a 'neutral' effect; so small that it is insignificant. Over time, mutations can be passed on from generation to generation, and this can cause changes to an organism through the process of **evolution**, like the X-gene in X-Men. Mutations exist in all of us, so what happens when these mutations affect your genes?

MISSING GENES: FRIEND OR FOE?

Missing genes as a mutation can cause disease. An example of this type of disease would be cystic fibrosis, which affects the lungs and requires lifetime medications, and in the most severe cases, lung transplants. Yet missing gene mutations can also be beneficial, for example, some people do not have working copies of a gene called **PCSK9**. Scientists observed individuals with this gene had almost no harmful cholesterol in their blood. Based on these findings, drug companies started to trial medicine that would 'block' or turn off the PCSK9 gene, and these drugs are currently undergoing testing for treatment of patients with high cholesterol in the USA. The lack of a gene called **SLC308A** means that an individual is half as likely to get diabetes as those with it, and those without working copies of **CCR5** are less likely to be infected with HIV.

DISEASE AND IMMUNITY

A disease known as sickle cell anaemia is caused by a mutated gene **HbS**. In order to suffer from the disease, you must hold two copies of the mutated gene, one from each of your parents. Some individuals only have one copy of the mutant gene, along with a normal **haemoglobin** gene. These individuals have less severe symptoms and if bitten by a mosquito have immunity to **malaria**.

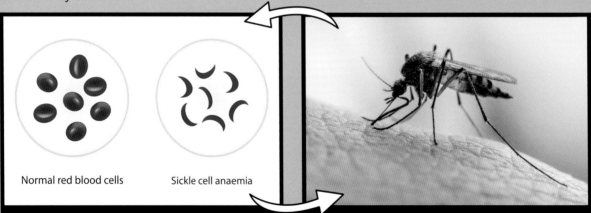

Normal red blood cells   Sickle cell anaemia

Figure 16: The mutation causing sickle cell anaemia means red blood cells form irregular moon shapes instead of round cells, however, it also gives the individual protection against malaria carried by mosquitoes.

HEALING POWERS

After a woman in Scotland had two operations and felt no pain afterwards, she was referred for tests. Scientists found two mutations that reduced her pain and anxiety, boosted her happiness and increased her wound healing. Jo Cameron, who is in her seventies, broke her arm when she was eight and didn't tell anyone for days until the bone in her arm began resetting at a strange angle. She can eat very hot Scotch Bonnet chilli peppers without pain, and when she injures herself she heals very rapidly. She has a mutation that reduces the activity of an **FAAH** gene, which makes an enzyme that breaks down a chemical called **anandamide** that works on pain sensation, mood and memory. A previously unknown gene mutation, scientists named it — wait for it — FAAH OUT!

This mutation caused chemicals that have a pain-killing property to build up in her system, meaning she has twice the levels of those in the general population! Scientists hope that by studying Jo's genes, they can look at ways to use genes to reduce pain and promote healing in others.

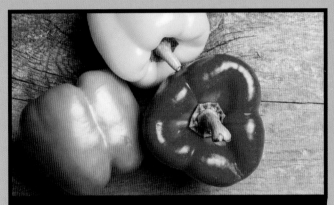

Figure 17: The heat from peppers is measured in Scoville Heat Units (SHU). A bell pepper might be a maximum of 100 SHU but Scotch Bonnets reach up to 350,000 SHU, which in an ordinary individual, would cause pain when eaten!

CONCLUSION

Superheroes started with philosophy and became reality - superhumans really do exist outside of comic books and movies! However, the effects may not be as extreme. We've seen that humans can show incredible strength and resilience and our bodies have unique and exciting ways to increase our potential (and we aren't very different to chimpanzees or bananas!) We know that mutations can be useful, and with continuing developments in genetic technology and our understanding of our own genetic code, scientists can use this knowledge to cure or prevent disease. As we understand ourselves better, we can achieve more and look forward to an amazing future!

PSYCHOLOGY OF SUPERHEROES

SARITA is a Principal Lecturer at the University of Central Lancashire. Sarita has investigated the psychobiology of behaviour over the last fifteen years, specifically focusing on how the brain functions (or doesn't) when we face life-threatening events. Sarita's research frequently means she finds herself in high-pressure environments, such as working with fire-fighters, people undergoing Helicopter Underwater Evacuation Training and other stress-inducing survival courses. In her spare time, Sarita enjoys doing stand-up comedy and public engagement talks.

INTRODUCTION

What makes a superhero? Is it the ability to fly? To have super strength? Access to advanced technology? Or does it take *more* than a superpower or special equipment? To really understand what makes a hero, we need to look beyond their superpowers and understand their psychological make-up. Being a superhero is more than just having enhanced abilities or access to alien technology. It is about being able to put others first, being fearless in the face of adversity and having the ability to carry on when all seems lost.

From the ancient Greeks and Egyptians, through to the present day, people have been interested in how the human mind works. However, until the late nineteenth century, **psychology** was considered to be a branch of philosophy and not a science. This changed in 1879 when Wilhelm Wundt set up the first experimental psychology laboratory at the University of Leipzig in Germany. Sigmund Freud, at the start of the twentieth century, provided an alternative to the scientific study of the human mind, with **psychoanalysis**. These two ideas, as well as John B. Watson's **behaviourist approach** (which suggested that psychology should focus on behaviours which were measurable and observable), further helped to establish psychology as a science.

Because of this, psychology is a comparatively young science compared to other disciplines, such as chemistry or physics, but it does have several different branches. Some focus on a specific topic area, such as **health psychology** or **forensic psychology**, whereas other branches use a specific framework to try to understand the human brain and behaviour. For example, the birth of the computer in the 1940s prompted the birth of **cognitive psychology** — which sees the brain as an information processor. Cognitive psychology, therefore, tries to replicate the different processes that the brain undertakes, such as memory or vision, to gain an understanding of how these processes work. The fact that psychology is such a young discipline makes it a very exciting time to be a psychologist!

Although psychology as a discipline has

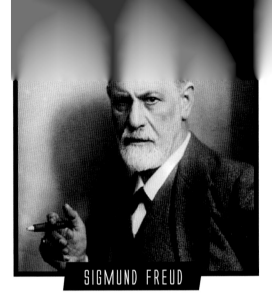

SIGMUND FREUD

been around since the late nineteenth century, the tools to investigate psychological processes are not that well developed. In fact, it was not until the early 1900s that we were first able to view the brain of someone while they were still alive. This technique, known as **pneumoencephalography**, was both risky and painful. It involved the cerebrospinal fluid around the brain being drained and replaced with air, for clear x-rays to be taken. It was not until the 1970s that safe, non-invasive brain imaging techniques became available. We now have several different methods that can provide us with detailed images of the brain, such as **computerised axial tomography (CAT)**, **magnetic resonance imaging (MRI)**, and **functional magnetic resonance imaging (fMRI)**. However, as brain scans are expensive and difficult to carry out, most psychologists use a range of self-reporting, observational methods, physiological measures and **cognitive tasks** (tasks that assess how well someone can perform a mental function such as a memory task) to understand someone's brain. But as the Agents of SHIELD frequently find out, a psych evaluation is not always worth the paper it is written on and there is still a lot we do not know about human brain functions.

Let's start by considering what the physical brain of a superhero may look like. Do their special powers and skills lead to physical differences in the brain? Or it is possible that having superpowers might lead to changes in the way in which the brain functions? To explore these two questions, we must first learn a little about the physical structure of the human brain. Figure 1 gives a top-down view of a normal brain which is divided into two parts (the left and right hemisphere). For the moment let us speculate that Earth-based humanoid superheroes have a similar physical brain shape to you and me, with their brain fitting inside the average human skull.

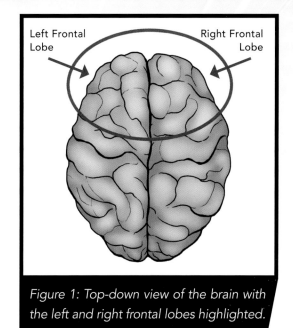

Figure 1: Top-down view of the brain with the left and right frontal lobes highlighted.

The two hemispheres of a normal brain are divided into four main areas: the **frontal**, **parietal**, **temporal** and **occipital** lobes. Neuroscientists and psychologists believe that they know some of the key functions which are undertaken by the four lobes, but the location of some brain functions are still elusive (see Figure 2).

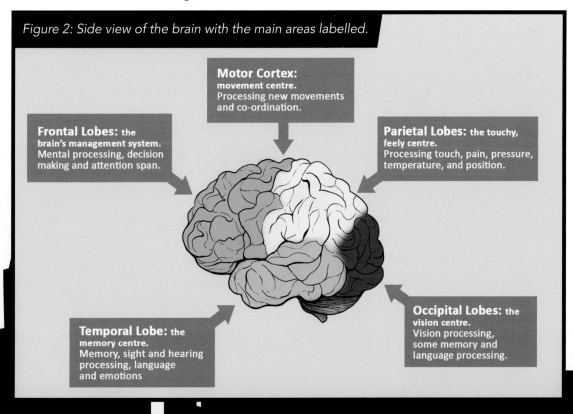

Figure 2: Side view of the brain with the main areas labelled.

Motor Cortex: movement centre. Processing new movements and co-ordination.

Frontal Lobes: the brain's management system. Mental processing, decision making and attention span.

Parietal Lobes: the touchy, feely centre. Processing touch, pain, pressure, temperature, and position.

Temporal Lobe: the memory centre. Memory, sight and hearing processing, language and emotions

Occipital Lobes: the vision centre. Vision processing, some memory and language processing.

However, no two brains are exactly alike. Even if a superhero's skull is the same size and shape as ours, their brain size and the way in which it functions might be completely different. For example, Einstein — one of the greatest scientists who ever lived — had a small brain even though his skull size was the same as an average adult male.

In fact, there are a group of people who have normal-sized skulls and function quite normally, but when we do brain scans appear to have no brains at all. These people are known as 'no-brainers' and they have a condition called **hydrocephalus** which means that their skull is filled with cerebrospinal fluid (a fluid which is found around the brain and spinal cord), leaving limited space for a brain (Figure 3). However, even though their brain volume is very small, some 'no-brainers' can walk, talk and live a normal life. In one case described in the medical journal *The Lancet*, a 44-year-old married, father of two who worked as a civil servant was found to have virtually no brain after having a scan to try and diagnose the cause of his leg weakness.

Therefore, the case of Einstein and the 'no-brainers' shows that the physical shape and size of a brain does not predict how well it will function. In the case of superheroes, it might be that they have an average-sized skull and brain but are capable of exceptional things. Doctor Strange, for example, has the skull size of an average male but can use his mind to open doors to different dimensions. Rocket Raccoon, on the other hand, has a physical brain size that is much smaller than the average human but most of the time appears to be highly intelligent. In contrast, having an extra-large head, like that of Karnak (an Inhuman) or Uatu (The Watcher) does not guarantee high levels of intelligence. In fact, a large cranial area does seem to be a risk factor for becoming a supervillain. For example, MODOK, The Leader (aka Samuel Sterns) and Sinestro (enemy of Green Lantern) all have larger than average heads.

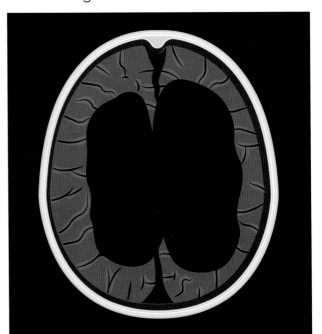

Figure 3: A diagram of a brain suffering from hydrocephalus.

ARE HEROES BORN OR MADE?

One of the great debates within psychology is the **nature/nurture** debate. Psychologists are still trying to figure out whether we are born with certain characteristics, such as being the brave and heroic type, or whether those behaviours are learnt after we are born. One way to try and work out what behaviours are genetic (nature) and which are the result of our environment (nurture) is to look at adoption studies (see Figure 4). Within the world of superheroes, one of the most famous cases of adoption is when Superman is taken in by Jonathan and Martha Kent. Superman, or Clark as he is named, develops the ability to fly; a skill that must be inherited from his biological family as no-one in his adoptive family has that ability.

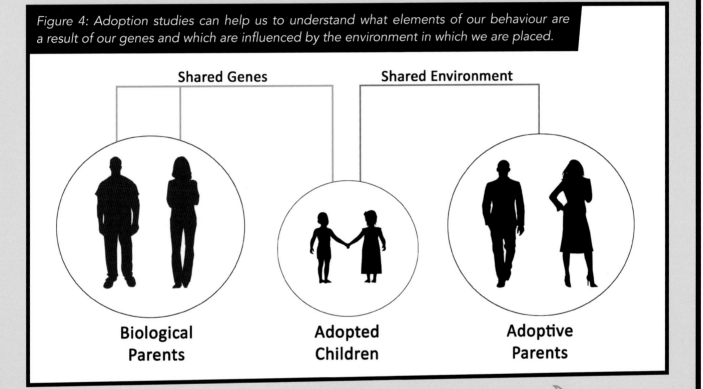

Figure 4: Adoption studies can help us to understand what elements of our behaviour are a result of our genes and which are influenced by the environment in which we are placed.

However, even adoption studies do not give us all the answers as to which behavioural traits are the result of our genetics and which are the result of our environment. This is because the environment can have an impact on our brains even before we are born! In one study, children born to mothers who had been pregnant during ice storms in Canada were found to be more fretful than their siblings. The process of the environment influencing unborn children is known as **prenatal programming**, which means that it is difficult to separate out the impact of genetic (nature) versus environmental (nurture) influences on our personality.

CAN WE LEARN TO BE A SUPERHERO?

Some superheroes have their powers from birth, whereas others unlock their abilities later in life because of a violent encounter with their environment. For Peter Parker, this was a bite from a radioactive spider and for the Inhumans, it was exposure to Terrigen crystals which activated latent genes. However, just having superpowers does not make you a superhero. For example, Sir Reginald Hargreeves, the Umbrella Academy children's guardian and mentor, is not very successful in developing superheroes who can control and use their superpowers responsibly. Even if superpowers are present from birth, training and developing the right skills to deal with the consequences of having powers is still needed.

It is much easier to learn new skills when we are young. For example, language learning is almost effortless when we are very young, with most toddlers picking up around ten new words every day. As we get older, our ability to learn new skills gets harder, and by the time we are twelve or thirteen years old our ability to learn a second language fluently is lost. This could explain why some superheroes start their training at a young age. For example, Black Widow was subjected to extensive martial arts and weapons training from a young age. As she was young when she started training, it is likely that she was able to pick up the skills she needed quicker and easier than if she had been older. Another example of a superhero who started their training young is Robin. Although Robin initially trained as a circus performer, his circus skills learnt in childhood enabled him to become an accomplished fighter as an adult.

The reason that we find it more difficult to pick up a new skill after adolescence is because of a process called **synaptic pruning**. Synapses are brain structures that allow the brain's cells to talk to each other. As we get older, our brain decides which skills are useful and which we are not going to need in adulthood. Once the brain has decided which skills we are not going to need, it carries out the process of pruning, where it gets rid of pathways that are not being used (See Figure 5).

Synaptic pruning is thought to cause some of the problem behaviours that we see in teenagers. As the brain is cutting different pathways, teenagers can find it hard to think

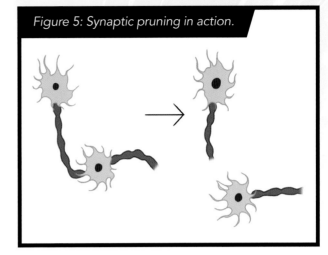

Figure 5: Synaptic pruning in action.

through the consequences of their actions. This is because the pathways which allow them to see the consequences of their behaviour are being reorganised. In a normal teenager's life, synaptic pruning can explain why risky behaviours such as excessive drinking or shoplifting are undertaken, as teenagers cannot think through the consequences of their actions. Of course, the risky behaviours of teenagers are even more dangerous if they have superpowers. For example, Negasonic Teenage Warhead may annoy Deadpool with her sulky teenage silences, but real problems will occur if she cannot think through the consequences of using her telekinetic detonation abilities irresponsibly. Another example of teenage superheroes suffering more severe consequences because of normal irresponsible teenage behaviour is Number Five from *The Umbrella Academy*. He refuses to listen to the warnings of his father, Sir Reginald Hargreeves, that he is not ready to time travel. He disobeys his father and ends up stuck in the future where he remains for several decades until he works out how to get back.

Although it can be harder to learn a new skill in later life, it is not impossible and environmental factors continue to have an impact on our brains throughout adulthood. Many environmental factors, such as nutrition, playing sport and even radioactive spider bites can change the shape of our brains. For example, if we undertake musical training for many years, we can see — with the use of brain scans — structural changes in areas such as the **motor cortex** (see Figure 2 on page 31). The structural changes seen as the result of music lessons appear to be associated with enhancements in certain functions, such as visual-spatial, verbal and mathematical abilities. In another example of **brain plasticity** (the term used to describe how the brain changes and adapts because of different experiences), psychologists have discovered that when London Taxi drivers learn the layout of all the roads and buildings in London, physical changes in

the brain regions involved in the recall of spatial information occur. Specifically, taxi drivers have been found to have an enlarged **hippocampus**, a structure important for memory which is found deep within the temporal lobes. Figure 6 below shows the location of the hippocampus within the brain.

Just as the brain structure of a taxi driver changes as they learn, a superhero's brain structure may also change as they learn to harness their superpowers or use specialist equipment.

Within the superhero world, training is needed to improve any superpower that requires movement. For example, when Scott Lang puts on the Ant-Man costume it takes time for him to master the ability to shrink and grow. Specifically, Scott needs to improve his **proprioception** — this is the ability to just know where your body, arms and legs are without having to think about it. We can speculate that one of

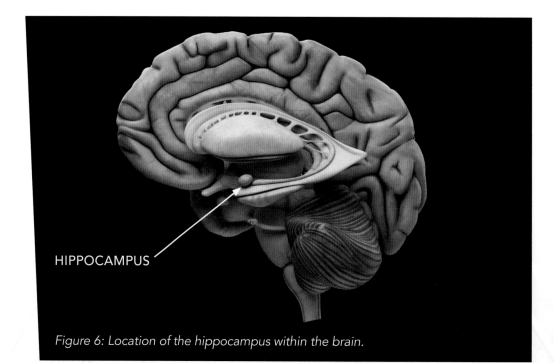

HIPPOCAMPUS

Figure 6: Location of the hippocampus within the brain.

the most important parts of the brain to support Scott's enhanced proprioception is the motor cortex, found at the back of the frontal lobes. Scott may also have physical changes in the area at the very front of the brain, known as the **pre-frontal cortex** (at the anterior of the frontal lobes), which is important for attention and decision-making. You can test your own proprioception by trying out the following exercise. Stand tall with your eyes closed and reach out your arms on each side.

Next, move your right hand and try to place your forefinger on your nose. Now move your other hand and try and place your other forefinger on your nose. Did you do it the first time? If you did — well done! If you missed your nose, don't worry, you can improve your proprioception with practice.

Superheroes may also have to enhance their proprioception abilities in order to use special equipment. Researchers have found that fencers and table tennis players have higher proprioceptive abilities in the arm that they use to hold their foil or table tennis bat compared to others. Therefore, it is possible that superheroes like Thor will need to have enhanced proprioception in his right arm so that he can sense where his hammer, Mjölnir, is in relation to his body at all times. Practice can enhance our proprioception, and so training in the use of all special equipment, from Iron Man's suit to Batman's utility belt, is essential. One way to dramatically *reduce* our proprioception, if you have ever seen a drunk person trying to walk, is to drink alcohol. Drunk superheroes are less likely to be able to use their equipment effectively and could potentially do great damage to themselves and others. If walking while drunk is dangerous, imagine what would happen if you tried to fly or teleport while under the influence of alcohol!

ENHANCING YOUR BRAIN WITH MEDITATION

Recently, neuropsychologists have discovered that undertaking **meditation** can increase people's mental abilities. Meditation, such as **mindfulness training**, has been shown to help people relax and can reduce levels of anxiety and depression. One simple mindfulness exercise you can try is called the **body scan** and details of how to carry out this exercise are given below in Figure 7.

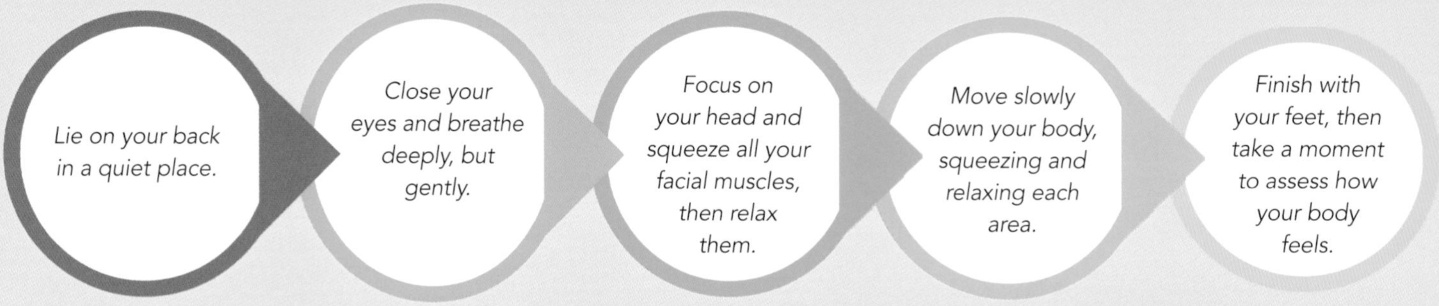

Lie on your back in a quiet place.

Close your eyes and breathe deeply, but gently.

Focus on your head and squeeze all your facial muscles, then relax them.

Move slowly down your body, squeezing and relaxing each area.

Finish with your feet, then take a moment to assess how your body feels.

Figure 7: Body scan mindfulness exercise.

A superhero who has used both physical and mental training to develop their superpowers is Doctor Strange. After his accident, he travels to Kamar-Taj to train under the guidance of Mordo and the Ancient One. Although some of Doctor Strange's special abilities come from his ownership of mystical objects, such as the Cloak of Levitation, his training at Kamar-Taj does appear to have unlocked additional brain functions that allow him to enter the Mirror Dimension. Although the majority of people undertaking mindfulness practice will not gain entry to other dimensions, researchers have found that mindfulness can cause physical changes in people's brain structure. For example, practising mindfulness daily for as little as eight weeks has been shown to increase grey matter within the brain regions which are responsible for learning, memory and the regulation of our emotions. If meditation is not something that you wish to try, research has also found that undertaking **resistance and cardiovascular training** (such as weightlifting or running), as well as coordination training (such as Tai Chi), can lead to changes in the way the brain works. Generally, people who undertake regular exercise have better functioning brains.

PREPARING FOR ACTION

Being a superhero takes more than having powers or having special equipment. To be a superhero you need to be able to make the right decisions, put others before yourself and show courage and leadership. Although a superhero may want to run away from danger, they are able to overcome that feeling and head straight into the heart of the battle. So how do superheroes cope with the dangerous situations that they find themselves in? According to John 'Lofty' Wiseman (the author of the *SAS Survival Handbook*), the ability to survive life-threatening events is fifteen per cent down to your practical knowledge, whereas your psychological make-up accounts for the other eighty-five per cent of your survival chances. Therefore, making sure that you are psychologically ready to face a threat could be even more important than your physical training.

One of the most commonly seen behaviours in emergency situations is people denying that anything bad is happening. People can even distort the danger signs to reassure themselves that they are not at any real risk. There have been cases of people who have failed to run away from active shooters as they have convinced themselves that the gunshots are just the sounds of fireworks or a car backfiring. However, most superheroes are alert to the threats that may occur and some superheroes band together to monitor for potential threats. For example, the Avengers Initiative and the Justice League of America's Watchtower were both set up so that threats can be monitored for, identified and dealt with.

Planning for an emergency is one thing, but how do the brain and body respond when we are in danger? In fact, the brain is always monitoring our environment for threats and the minute that we perceive a threat, the brain passes information to an area known as the **amygdala**, which is responsible for the processing of emotional stimuli. If the amygdala confirms that the body is facing a serious threat, then the **hypothalamus** triggers two main physiological systems that are designed to enhance self-preservation. The role of these two systems is to help the body to cope with the threat it is facing. The first system that is activated is the **sympathomedullary pathway (SAM)** which is responsible for what is known as the **Fight or Flight Response** (See Figure 8).

The actions of the SAM pathway lead to physiological changes. For example, the body needs more oxygen in order to fuel an increase in physical activity. Therefore, SAM activation causes the airways in our lungs to expand which increases our oxygen intake. SAM activation triggers the release of adrenaline which then causes glucose to be released from the liver. This glucose helps us fuel our physical response to the threat. In addition, our heart begins to beat faster to allow the blood to be pumped quicker to the brain and muscles. The extra glucose and oxygen within the blood can improve our brain's ability to process and respond to events as well as ensure we stay alert to danger. For some superheroes, the

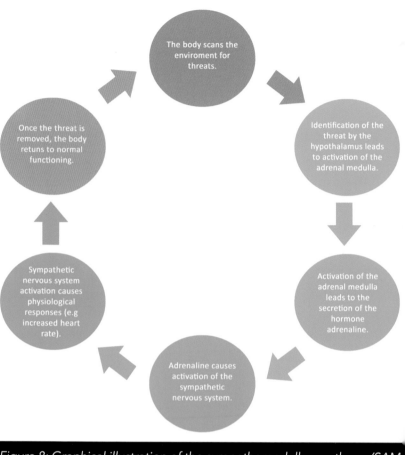

Figure 8: Graphical illustration of the sympathomedullary pathway (SAM)

triggering of the SAM pathway can lead to the body undertaking major physiological changes. For example, in the case of Bruce Banner, the activation of the SAM pathway leads to a release of adrenaline which increases his heart rate. Once he reaches 200 beats per minute (which is much higher than the human resting heart rate of between sixty and eighty beats) he is transformed into Hulk. Bruce Banner's change into Hulk can be useful and help him to deal with immediate danger. However, Bruce's transformation appears to reduce his cognitive capacity and so Hulk's decision-making and language processing appear to be reduced.

Other superheroes may also find that activation of the SAM pathway changes the way that their bodies work and gives them the extra energy that they need to deal with a situation. As SAM activation gives the body additional fuel (in the form of additional glucose and oxygen) superheroes may show improvements in their ability to use their superpowers. For example, in *Black Lightning*, Jennifer Pierce can use her ability to project energy bolts from her hands effectively for the first time when her mother is threatened.

If a person remains under threat for over twenty minutes, a second system kicks in — the **hypothalamic-pituitary-adrenal axis (HPA axis)** (see Figure 9). The HPA axis is designed to maintain a slightly longer-term response to a threat, as the responses generated by the SAM pathway are high cost in terms of energy.

Activation of the HPA axis increases the levels of a hormone called **cortisol**, which helps the body to maintain a high level of glucose in the blood.

Once the brain believes that the threat is no longer present, levels of cortisol start to reduce, and the body returns to normal. In the case of Hulk, the lullaby sung by Black Widow helps him to know that the threat is over and that he can return to his human form.

Although activation of the SAM pathway and the HPA axis can help to keep us safe, the changes they cause can have negative impacts on our mental functioning. Returning to Hulk, his decline in mental functioning is very marked, however other superheroes are able to stay cool, calm and collected. For example, Shuri (princess of Wakanda), can put her emotions to one side and continue to undertake complex engineering feats even when her home of Wakanda is under attack by Thanos's soldiers in *Avengers: Infinity War*.

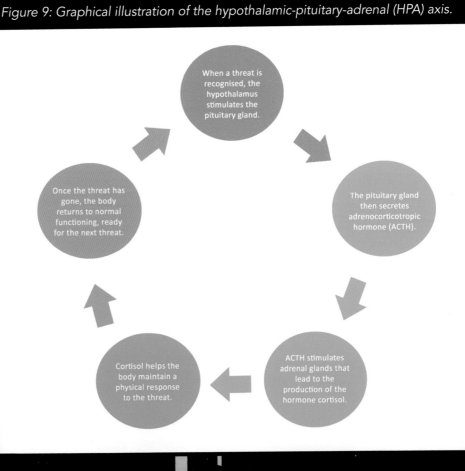

Figure 9: Graphical illustration of the hypothalamic-pituitary-adrenal (HPA) axis.

PERSONALITY TRAITS AND SUPERHEROES

As well as being able to keep cool in a crisis, in order to be a good superhero you need to have the right personality traits alongside the right superpowers. If a person does not have these traits, then they may not be able to use their superpowers for good, or worse still, they may become a supervillain. Psychologists have identified five main personality factors (the Big Five) which are universally present in both Western and non-Western cultures. It is thought that people fall between two extreme points on a scale for each of the five factors. So, what personality traits should superheroes have in order to ensure that they are able to rise to the challenge of saving the world?

OPENNESS TO EXPERIENCE:
On this trait, people range from being very curious to being very cautious. Generally, people with superpowers tend to be on the adventurous side and are very open to new experiences. An example of this would be during *Avengers: Infinity War* when Peter Parker sneaks aboard Ebony Maw's spaceship when instructed to return to Earth by Tony Stark.

CONSCIENTIOUSNESS:
This refers to how organised and effective people are. Some people are highly organised and like to follow the rules, whereas others prefer to be disorganised and spontaneous.

Characters with the latter traits appear to have an increased likelihood of becoming a supervillain, for example, the Joker. Although some of our superheroes are spontaneous, impulsive and could even be labelled as reckless, they all tend to follow a code of conduct which keeps them on the side of good. Even Green Arrow, who has a disregard for the law, has an internal personal code that keeps him on the straight and narrow.

EXTRAVERSION:
People vary on the extraversion scale from being the outgoing type who loves being the life and soul of the party, through to those who are more introverted and enjoy their own company. Superheroes tend to be drawn from the whole spectrum of the extraversion scale. Many have extravert tendencies as they are drawn to the action and enjoy being the centre of attention. In the Marvel Cinematic Universe (*MCU*) one of the most extroverted super heroes is Iron Man who enjoys the celebrity status that his crime-fighting brings him. However, other superheroes, such as the shy teenage Spider-Man, are more introverted, but this does not seem to be a barrier to them carrying out their superhero duties — they just might not go to the party afterwards celebrating their victory.

AGREEABLENESS: High levels of agreeableness are associated with being caring, cooperative and considerate. People who are less agreeable have low levels of empathy and little concern for the health and well-being of others. Generally, superheroes are selfless and put their lives on the line to save ours. Both Captain America and Superman show high levels of agreeableness and empathy which make them good leaders for their respective teams.

NEUROTICISM: People who are high on the neuroticism scale tend to be very nervous and lacking in confidence. Those who are low in the neuroticism scale tend to have more confidence and less anxiety regarding the decisions they made. Generally, superheroes tend to have low levels of neuroticism and can deal confidently with even the most stressful of situations. In fact, superheroes like Black Widow show a remarkable ability to stay cool, calm and collected. This is important, because who wants a superhero who goes to pieces the first time they meet a supervillain?

Alongside the personality traits listed above, we should also consider some negative personality characteristics, which fall within what is known as **the dark triad**. This is made up of three characteristics: **psychopathy**, **Machiavellianism** and **narcissism**.

PSYCHOPATHY: People with psychopathic traits show low empathy levels and little remorse for their behaviour. This arguably separates a superhero from a supervillain, as without empathy it is very easy for those with superpowers to use their abilities for evil, as they are unable to understand the impact their actions are having on other people.

MACHIAVELLIANISM: People with Machiavellian personality traits tend to be manipulative and are willing to exploit others. People with this trait generally lack a moral code and have a high level of self-interest and deception. One example of a supervillain who scores highly on the Machiavellian personality trait is Ego the living planet, from *Guardians of the Galaxy Vol. 2*, who was only interested in using Star-Lord as a power source to terraform all other planets and not in having a healthy father-son relationship.

NARCISSISM: People who have a high level of narcissism tend to lack empathy and have a high level of entitlement. Generally, narcissists do not make good companions and are not good at being team players as they are just out for themselves. Unfortunately, Tony Stark is an example of someone who has narcissistic traits. When Black Widow completes a psychological evaluation, she concludes that Tony Stark has compulsive behaviours, is prone to self-destructive tendencies as well as being a narcissist. Although Tony does have a sense of entitlement and can fail to consider the thoughts and feelings of others in his team, he does also show insight regarding the impact of his behaviours. As a result of this insight, he is able to show positive behaviours such as handing over Stark Industries to Pepper Potts in *Iron Man 3*.

SUPERHERO TEAMS – IS IT BETTER TO SAVE THE EARTH WITH A FRIEND?

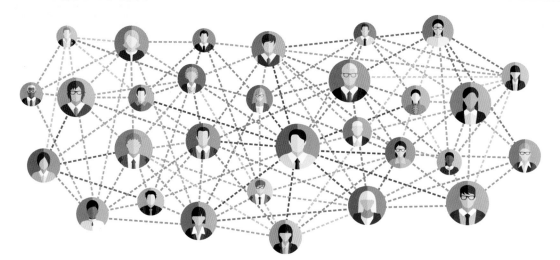

It is very rare for people to live their lives on their own. Humans are social creatures and most of us enjoy the company of others, and the family and friends whom we rely on for love and support are known as our **social support network**. Having this group of people who are able to give us both practical and emotional support has been found to be beneficial for both physical health and mental wellbeing. It is thought that social support acts as a 'buffer' protecting people from negative events. For example, researchers have found that if you undertake a stressful task — such as public speaking — with a friend present, your heart rate will not increase as much as if you undertake the task on your own. Researchers have suggested that having a good network of friends and family to call on in times of need can help us to adopt more positive coping strategies. For example, students with higher levels of social support have been found to be less likely to turn to alcohol to help them cope with exam stress.

Social support is also important in times of crisis. People with better social support networks have been found to recover quicker after exposure to traumatic events. This might explain why superheroes form into teams. Groups of superheroes such as the Justice League of America, the Avengers Initiative, or the Guardians of the Galaxy, form tight-knit teams who can support each other. As well as offering practical help and advice, they offer each other emotional support; many superhero teams often became very close and more like a family than a group of friends. This may be because families can have difficulty understanding and accepting superpowers, therefore it is easier for superheroes to bond with people who are having similar experiences to them.

Yet researchers have also found that sometimes having family and friends around us is not always a positive experience. It is not hard to remember how annoying a sibling can be if you are stuck in the house with them over a wet weekend! In one study, researchers found that when men were asked to undertake a stressful public speaking task, it was less stressful when they were supported by their female partners. However, when the task was reversed, and the women undertook the speaking task, the support of a male partner did not seem to have the same beneficial effects. We cannot always assume that social support will have a positive benefit, and this is also true in the superhero world. For example, although Loki is family, Thor does not often find him helpful or supportive — quite the opposite in fact!

PICKING THE RIGHT TEAM

So how do we go about picking the right people to join teams? Selecting the right people to be our friends in the everyday world is an important and complex task. But when superheroes are selecting people who they are prepared to work with and rely on, the stakes are much higher. In the past, when agencies like NASA selected people to train as astronauts, there has been an assumption that it is possible to spot the 'right stuff' in a candidate. The 'right stuff' has been defined as people who are independent, expressive and driven to work. Sometimes it is easier to spot people with the 'wrong stuff' as they are competitive, impatient and irritable, or even those with 'no stuff' who have low levels of motivation, are unassertive or have high levels of verbal aggression. However, there is a growing awareness that identifying people with the 'right stuff' is not a straightforward task.

One way in which teams of superheroes could be formed is by using psychological screening as part of a selection procedure. The first problem with forming superheroes into teams is that only a limited number of people have superpowers, so there is a limited pool of people to draw from. The second problem is more difficult to overcome; it must be mentioned that most people with superpowers appear to have some major personality flaws. In fact, some superheroes, such as Deadpool, are just not team players and so will

never be able to be a successful member of a team. Problems can also arise if team members can't decide on a leader; challenges over leadership can cause conflict which can affect the whole team. For example, in *Captain America: Civil War*, both Tony Stark and Steve Rogers have strong ideas about how the Avengers should operate, and their conflict has a negative impact on the whole Avengers team. However, when a team is working effectively, shares a common goal and has good leadership, the team members can benefit from the social support available. One example of an atypical but fully functioning superhero team is the Guardians of the Galaxy. This team proves that a diverse number of beings — a half-human half-alien, an alien orphan, a tree-like humanoid, a warrior seeking revenge for his family's death and a genetically engineered raccoon-like creature — can all work together effectively.

THE BURDEN OF BEING A SUPERHERO

Superheroes work hard to chase down the bad guys, rescue the innocent and save the world. They risk both physical and mental assaults and are frequently in fights or are kidnapped and tortured. Continual exposure to traumatic events can have a marked impact on mental wellbeing. Within the general population, around five to ten per cent of people will develop a clinical disorder after exposure to trauma. The condition is known as **post-traumatic stress disorder (PTSD)** and has several characteristics which are detailed below in Figure 10.

Everyday superheroes, such as emergency service workers (police, firefighters and paramedics) deal with difficult situations daily. Rates of PTSD in emergency services workers have been found to be higher than the public, suggesting that people who have self-selected to work in challenging environments are not immune to the impact on their mental health. Therefore, it is quite possible that although superheroes may have high levels of bravery, their mental health may also suffer as a result of their experiences. For example, Steve Rogers appears to suffer from some of the symptoms of PTSD, as he has trouble sleeping and flashbacks relating to his plane crash.

Figure 10: Checklist of PTSD symptoms.

Re-Experiencing	Reliving the trauma can take the form of images, nightmares or flashbacks.
Avoidance	Avoiding situations, places or actions that remind the person of the traumatic event.
Hyperarousal	High levels of anxiety which means that people consistently feel 'on edge' and unable to relax.
Emotional Numbing	People may try to block out all feelings and become withdrawn.
Mood Changes	Some people can become depressed or anxious.
Substance Misuse	People may attempt to control or block out their feelings by turning to drink or drugs.

So how can we help people after exposure to a traumatic event? The most important thing to remember is that it is normal to have some adverse effects after being exposed to trauma. Yet in about 90-95% of cases, people will be able to recover with the help of friends and family and not require professional help. That is why most psychologists suggest a period of 'watchful waiting' to see whether people can deal with the impact of the trauma on their own or whether they need some additional support.

However, if people are not showing signs of recovery after around four to six weeks it might be time to consider some professional help. Interventions can include medication, such as antidepressants, or talking therapies, such as cognitive behavioural therapy.

POST-TRAUMATIC GROWTH

Friedrich Nietzsche (who you may remember from Cat's chapter!) suggests that 'What doesn't kill you makes you stronger' and some people who have been exposed to trauma say that their experiences have had some positive effects on their lives. These positive effects are referred to as **post-traumatic growth** and highlight how experiencing trauma does not always have negative consequences. People who experience post-traumatic growth say that their experiences have increased their levels of confidence and their self-belief. They also report that their relationships with family and friends have been strengthened and they have a new determination to 'seize the day'. Many superheroes are born out of traumatic starts. For example, Batman chose a life of crime-fighting after witnessing the murder of his parents. For some superheroes, the drive to fight evil and help others is born out of their own traumatic experiences.

CONCLUSION

The discipline of psychology can help us to understand what it really takes to become a superhero. For example, psychology can help us to understand how the brain of a superhero may differ from the brain of someone without superpowers. In addition, the nature/nurture debate within psychology can help us to explore whether superheroes are born (Superman born with the ability to fly) or made (Black Widow undertaking extensive training). Psychology also allows us to consider how factors, such as upbringing, personality traits and team dynamics, can all shape how someone with superpowers can turn into a superhero!

ADDITIONAL FACT - MESSING WITH YOUR BRAIN

Some superheroes and supervillains appear to have the ability to interfere with people's brains and can cause their victims to see and experience phenomena which are not physically present. Both Fay Moffit (Lady Spellbinder) and Scarlet Witch (Wanda Maximoff) appear to be able to directly manipulate the brains of others, causing visual and auditory hallucinations. But is it possible to induce hallucinations in people when you don't have superpowers? One neurosurgeon in the 1950s, Wilder Penfield, was able to induce visual or auditory hallucinations in his patients, but the technique used was very invasive. Penfield used an electrical probe to directly stimulate the brains of epileptic patients who were undergoing neurosurgery. As the **neurons** (brain cells — you'll learn more about these in Matt and Adam's chapter!) within our brains use electrical signals to send messages to each other, Penfield was able to trigger certain areas of the brain into working. As a result of his research, he was able to work out the function of specific regions of the brain. Some of Penfield's patients recalled very vivid memories whereas others experienced smells or the sensation of someone stroking the back of their hand. Penfield's techniques were, however, deemed too invasive to use, so he relied on people undertaking neurosurgery in order to open the skull ready for the electrical stimulation. More recently, psychologists have developed a new technique called **transcranial magnetic**

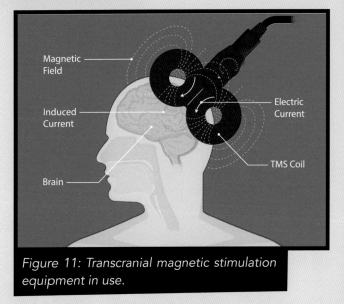

Figure 11: Transcranial magnetic stimulation equipment in use.

stimulation (TMS) that allows non-invasive stimulation of the brain. Above in Figure 11 is a diagram of this procedure.

TMS, unlike previous electrical stimulation techniques, does not require the probe to touch the brain directly. Instead, a rapidly changing current is delivered via a small coil of wire placed directly on the participant's scalp. The technique is painless and although it can temporarily lead to certain areas of the brain not working, no lasting damage has been recorded. TMS is mainly used to knock out areas of the brain (temporarily) in order to see what functions that particular area of the brain is responsible for. It is possible that individuals with the superpower to cause hallucinations could be causing neuro-electronic stimulation in different areas of the brain. For example, Scarlet Witch may be stimulating the temporal areas in people's brains which induces hallucinations.

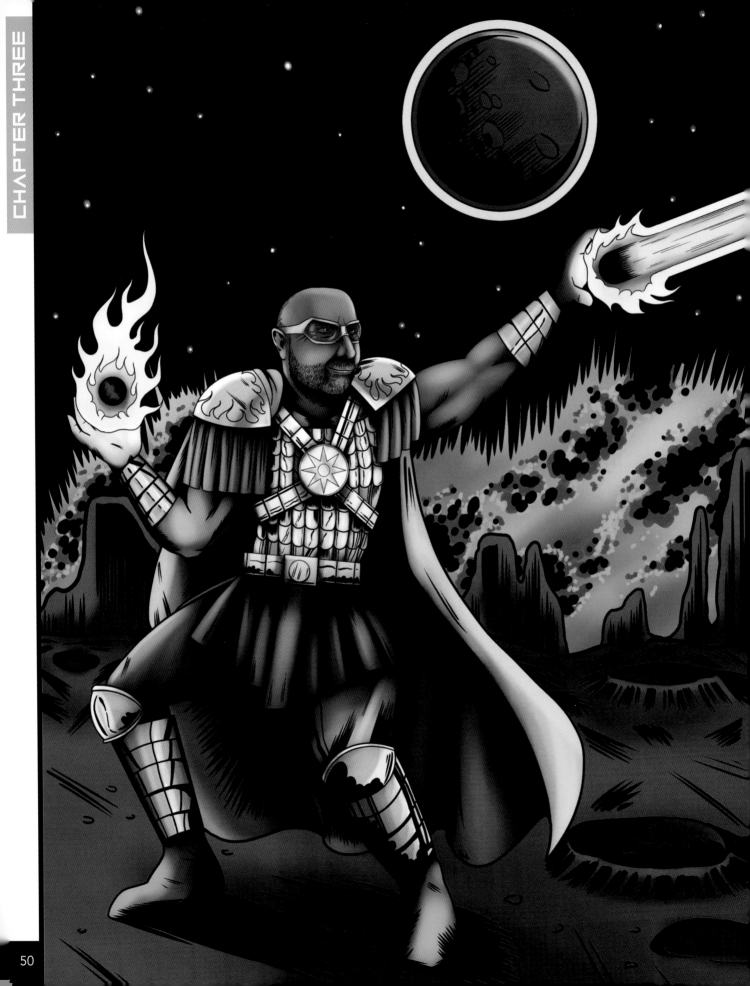

ALIEN WORLDS

ROBERT is a Professor of Solar Physics and is a world-leading expert on the Sun and its interaction with Earth. As well as collaborating with NASA colleagues on their sounding rocket programme, Robert is a Leadership Fellow in Public Engagement with the Science and Technology Facilities Council, specifically working with young people in Blackpool, Lancashire. Robert has helped set a public engagement Guinness World Record and collaborated with several artists to approach engagement with science research in new and creative ways. He is married to Heather, has two teenage children (Matthew and Emma), attends a local church in Preston as well as being a season ticket holder for Preston North End football club.

INTRODUCTION

On top of enhanced abilities, amazing technology and credibility-bending physics, superhero stories have introduced a science topic that challenges our very understanding of the Universe itself. Without a second thought, characters often accept that extraterrestrial creatures not just exist but are commonplace throughout the cosmos.

These superhero exploits introduce us to a universe teeming not just with life but with intelligent beings in every shape and form imaginable and possessing technology far superior to our own.

So, in this chapter we ask ourselves — what are the chances that alien life could evolve elsewhere in our galaxy and would that life be intelligent? Also, if extraterrestrial life does exist, how could they travel the vast distances across different star systems and end up in our own terrestrial neighbourhood?

There are strong arguments that the detection of extraterrestrial intelligence would be the greatest discovery in the history of humankind, changing our view of humanity's place in the Universe. But given what we can currently observe, can we begin to estimate the likelihood of there being life out there? Or putting it another way, what are the chances we are very alone?

It was in the 1960s when the astronomer Frank Drake put forward a simple way to estimate the likely number of intelligent extraterrestrial species there may be in our Milky Way galaxy that are actively communicating into space. And the way to do this was by considering the possible detection of alien **radio waves**.

Since the turn of the century, humankind has been increasingly dependent on the use of radio waves for communication. We generate these waves by creating regular increases and decreases in electrical currents within circuits. These changes, otherwise known as **oscillations**, create radio waves that move easily through the air. Whether we are broadcasting radio or television signals, a receiving unit captures the radio waves in an electrical conductor, generating a corresponding electrical current of the same frequency as the incoming radio wave. Encoded in the transmitted radio wave is information that requires decoding when the radio message is received.

However, these radio waves continue to travel past their destinations and go easily through the vacuum of space. In fact, our accumulated radio communications have been 'leaking out' from Earth in an ever-expanding sphere of radio noise. Earthlings have been shouting out about their presence in this part of the Galaxy via a man-made bubble of radio signals inflating out at the speed of light, waiting for 'someone' to detect it. By the start of the twenty-first century, broadcasts of simple clicks of Morse code were about 120 light-years away from Earth (the edge of the bubble). At about eighty light-years, the first television signals would be picked up, while 'anyone' at a distance of just over fifty light-years could start watching the first-ever exploits of Superman on television!

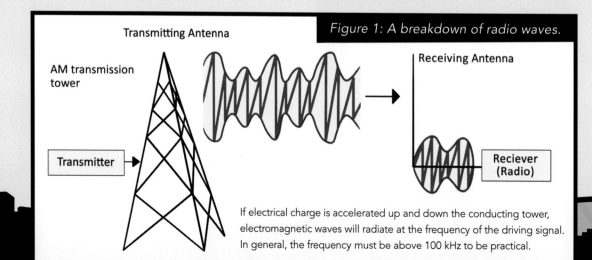

Figure 1: A breakdown of radio waves.

Transmitting Antenna

AM transmission tower

Transmitter

Receiving Antenna

Reciever (Radio)

If electrical charge is accelerated up and down the conducting tower, electromagnetic waves will radiate at the frequency of the driving signal. In general, the frequency must be above 100 kHz to be practical.

On top of this, our night sky is filled with objects that also naturally send out radio waves. Virtually all astronomical objects emit radio radiation in some form. Capturing these specific radio signals here on Earth allows astronomers to examine how these bodies work, allowing the 'listener' to 'hear' radio signals that reach our planet. To us here on Earth, our Sun is a powerful radio emitter, mainly due to the fact that it is our closest star and it sends out radiation right across the **electromagnetic spectrum**. However, other radio sources that are many millions of light-years away can also be colossal in the volume of radio waves they emit. Some of the strongest signals come from **pulsars** (known as lighthouses of the universe, these are rapidly rotating neutron stars that pulse radiation) and **quasars** (distant galaxies with a fluctuating intensity of radiation that are thought to be powered by supermassive black holes). These radio signals can easily pass through Earth's clouds and be detected by large radio antenna or dishes on the ground. One of the most famous radio telescopes in the world is the Lovell

Figure 2: The Lovell Telescope.

Telescope at Jodrell Bank, just outside of Manchester, United Kingdom.

Drake soon realised that he could hunt for aliens by trying to detect the radio emissions from extraterrestrial races that would be separate from these natural radio emitters. This got the astronomy community thinking about the range of scientific challenges that needed to be addressed if extraterrestrial life were to arise elsewhere in the Galaxy and be at an evolutionary stage to be able to be observed as **radio active**!

From all this information, the **Drake equation** was created. At a basic level, the equation is like an 'extraterrestrial recipe for life' aiming to provide an educated guess on a possible number of intelligent civilisations in our Milky Way galaxy by using the latest estimates for a range of important ingredients.

The Drake Equation can be written as follows. If **N** is the *estimated number of intelligent civilisations in the Milky Way galaxy*, we have that;

$$N = R \times f_p \times N_e \times f_L \times f_i \times fc \times L.$$

You might be thinking that looks a little complicated, but don't worry! In the following, we will break down each ingredient one at a time and then assign possible values to them. As we shall see, these values are changing all the time as our scientific knowledge increases.

THE BIRTHING OF STARS

The first parameter **R** is defined as the birth rate of suitable stars in the Milky Way galaxy, measured as the number of stars born per year. It is not the case that all stars simply existed immediately after the **Big Bang** or that all stars are exactly the same. Galaxies are essentially incredibly large collections of many different types of stars, with the earliest stars beginning to form about 100 million years or so after the Big Bang. Looking at the age and composition of the stars as well as how they are scattered within a host galaxy provides astronomers with a type of 'barcode' to understand the galaxy's history and evolution.

Figure 3: A spiral galaxy.

An individual star is born within a cloud of dust and gas, a large part of which consists of **hydrogen**. The unsteady movement of the material in the cloud gives rise to pockets of sufficiently denser material. Gas and dust particles start to draw closer to each other under the pull of gravity. Eventually, the cloud begins to collapse inwards on itself and the material at the centre starts to heat up significantly, forming what is known as a **protostar**. Then, as more material falls onto the surface of the protostar, the pressure on the material in the centre increases until **nuclear fusion** is ignited. When fusion occurs, **hydrogen nuclei** get squeezed together under incredibly high temperatures and pressures to create one form of a **helium nucleus**. In the process, a very small amount of mass is converted into pure energy. Once underway, fusion forms the dense heart (or core) of an actual star. After all the hydrogen has been used up, helium fuel 'burning' takes over which in turn creates **beryllium** that decays to **carbon**. This process can continue (carbon burning) to produce oxygen, nitrogen, magnesium etc and the manufacturing process continues.

The rate at which a star expends its fuel depends upon how large the star is. All in, our Sun is a pretty ordinary, bog-standard star. It appears to be about five billion years old and is approximately halfway through its lifetime. However, there are far larger stars that burn their fuel much more quickly. For example, a star ten times the size of the Sun would use up its fuel around 1,000 times quicker

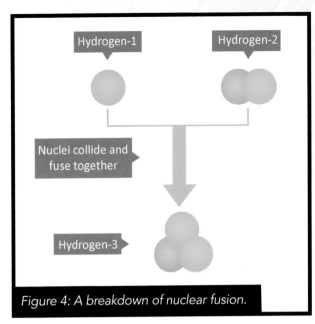

Figure 4: A breakdown of nuclear fusion.

than its solar cousin. As a consequence, the more massive star will exhaust its hydrogen fuel supply in a little under 100 million years, significantly less than the apparent lifetime of our Sun.

These larger stars violently explode off their outer layers seconds after the last bit of fuel has been consumed; this what is known as a **supernova,** the brightest, most dynamic display of natural ferocity in the Universe. With the brightness of a billion suns, the heavier elements created in the star get flung forcefully throughout space and subsequently form part of the dust and gas that forms other stars, a form of stellar recycling.

Of course, as this stellar formation process continues, not all of the cloud material ends up as part of a star. It is easy to come to the conclusion that the vast space between stellar bodies is completely empty. However, what is left over after a star is formed can remain as interstellar dust (including tiny solid particles of carbon, silicon and oxygen), but can also become planets, asteroids, or comets. It is the case that the very elements that make up everything on planet Earth were created billions of years ago in the nuclear furnace of exploding stars!

One way of classifying the rich variety of stars we observe in the night sky is to use something called a **Hertzsprung-Russell diagram.** With the star's temperature on the horizontal axis (in Kelvin) versus how bright it is on the vertical axis (or luminosity), an H-R diagram allows astronomers to follow the evolution of stars as they burn their fuel and evolve from one type of star to another.

Figure 5: A glowing stellar nursery revealing the birth of new protostars.

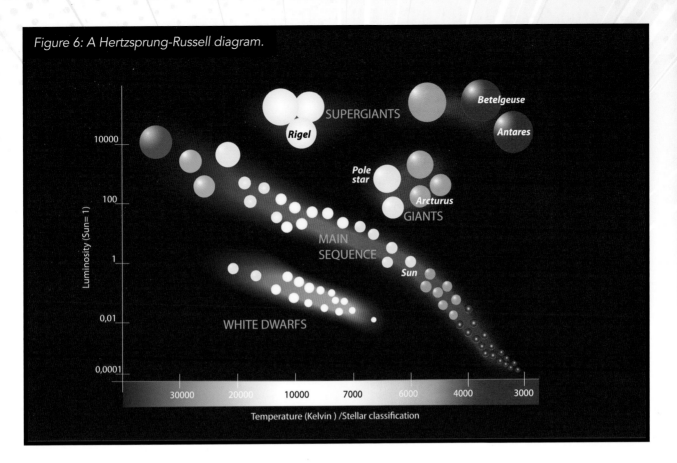

Figure 6: A Hertzsprung-Russell diagram.

For example, consider the case of our Sun. It is classified in the H-R diagram as a yellow dwarf star and is the yardstick by which we measure all other stellar objects. At approximately five billion years old, the Sun is having a bit of a mid-life crisis! Right now the star is not too active and doesn't change in brightness much – this is very good for us here on Earth. However, things will not always be like that. As the Sun continues to use up its hydrogen fuel, its brightness will increase. In about five billion years that fuel will deplete and our star will begin burning helium. Its outer layers will expand outwards, and our Sun will evolve to be a **red giant**. Estimates appear to show that at this stage the Sun will be so large that its outermost layers could envelop the Earth.

It will then 'blow off' these layers and cool to become a compact **white dwarf** before fading to black over trillions of years. But please don't worry — there are billions of years to go before this happens!

Coming back to the Drake Equation, **R** is concerned with 'suitable stars'. This can mean several things, including the star being stable for significant periods of time (likely many tens, if not hundreds of millions of years) and being far from becoming a supernova. So, after all the above are considered, the current estimates from NASA and the European Space Agency (ESA) for **R** are between one and a half and three stars per year — let's be generous and use an upper limit of three suitable star births annually in the Milky Way.

PLANETARY HIDE AND SEEK

The next ingredient **Fp** is the fraction of stars that have planetary systems associated with them. We call these extra-solar planets or exoplanets for short. The relatively new astronomical discipline of planet-hunting has dramatically increased our knowledge of these **exoplanets**.In fact, since their first detection in the mid-1990s, there has now been thousands of exoplanets discovered.

The ground-breaking space mission that accelerated our collection of detected exoplanets was NASA's Kepler Observatory. Kepler observations use the basic fact that when a planet travels in front of a star as viewed from the position of the observer, there is a tiny but measurable dip in the overall brightness of that star. We can occasionally see this from Earth in our own solar system as there are two planets in closer orbits to the Sun than ourselves. If the conditions are lined up correctly, Mercury and Venus can be observed as small black dots that crawl across the bright solar disc of the Sun. This journey of a planet between the host star and the observer is called a **transit**.

In the case of observing a planetary transit around stars other than the Sun, the detectable change in a star's brightness will be minuscule, sometimes a reduction in about 1/10,000th of the stellar brightness over several hours! Once detected, by applying basic knowledge of planetary motion, it can be estimated how long the exoplanet takes to orbit the star as well as its size and mass.

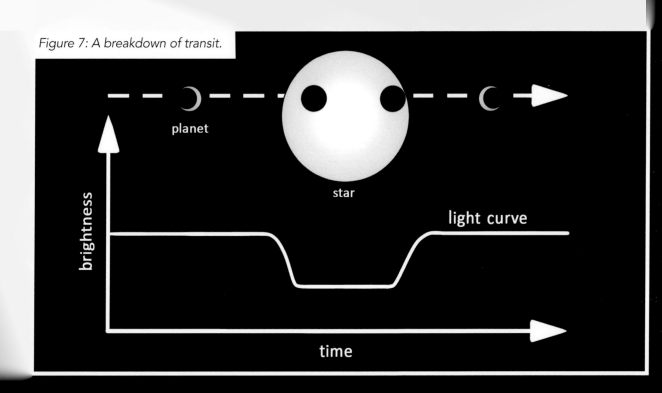

Figure 7: A breakdown of transit.

brightness

planet

star

light curve

time

Since the start of 2019, our exoplanet tally is near 4,000, so it can now be argued that virtually all stars are likely to be orbited by planets. Thus, let's be generous and put $f_p=1$; that is, if we have a star, there is at least one planet associated with it.

LOCATION, LOCATION, LOCATION

The Drake Equation does not simply use an estimate on the number of planets; we also need to know how many of these (the value **Ne**) exist in the star's **habitable zone**. This is a spherical region of space around a star where the temperature and atmospheric pressure of a planet residing in the zone are such that liquid water can be sustained at the planetary surface. If Ego the Living Planet wanted to know where to set up home, a habitable zone would be very necessary!

From the overall brightness and temperature of the host star, it is possible to provide an estimate for the characteristic temperature at the orbit of the exoplanet itself. Our own terrestrial homeworld is an excellent example of a habitable zone planet, but now other potential exoplanets have been detected that also reside in these very special habitable sectors. And one of these is around our next nearest star.

Alpha Centauri is the closest star system to our solar system at just over four **light-years** away. It's important to note that a light year is not a measure of time, but rather a measure of distance; it is the distance light can travel in a year. Light is the fastest moving thing in the universe, travelling at about 300,000 kilometres per second or around 9,400,000,000,000 kilometres (or 9.4 x 10^{12} kilometres) in one year. Four times that seems a long way to our nearest neighbour!

Alpha Centauri is a triple star system, with one star called **Rigil Kentaurus** (also known as Alpha Centauri A), a second called **Tolliman** (Alpha Centauri B) and a third named **Proxima Centauri** (Alpha Centauri C). There has been an exoplanet detected in Proxima Centauri's habitable zone. Imaginatively named Proxima Centauri B, this exoplanet resides at a distance of seven and a half million kilometres from the star, is about thirty per cent larger than Earth and makes a complete orbit in just over eleven Earth days. Even if technically Proxima Centauri B is in the habitable zone, disappointingly it is likely that the force of material streaming out from its parent star would strip the atmosphere off the exoplanet or not allow an atmosphere to form in the first place. We term this flow of material from a star the **stellar wind**. In this case, Proxima Centuari's is about two thousand times greater than our Sun's solar wind.

The case of Proxima Centauri B shows us that that we have to be careful about determining a range of values for **Ne** (the number of habitable exoplanets). A reasonable portion of detected exoplanets appear to be gas giants like Jupiter or Saturn, who have close orbits to their parent star, raising doubt that life-hosting rocky worlds could exist nearby in similar orbital paths. Along with the need for the host star to likely have long periods of not being too active, this means that current estimates range between ten to twenty per cent of stars having exoplanets that could survive in a star's habitable zone. Thus, again being positive, let's set **Ne** = 0.2.

WHAT IS (INTELLIGENT) LIFE ANYWAY?

Next in the Drake Equation is the term f_L, defined as the fraction of habitable planets where life comes into being. This parameter is largely unknown as currently we only have one data point to work with — planet Earth. That said, the rich diversity of life in our world would appear to suggest that given any favourable conditions, life could arise.

However, it is likely that if alien life is out there, it would initially resemble bacteria or simple cellular creatures that we are familiar with on Earth. It is estimated that unicellular organisms arose about four billion years ago and likely remained the dominant form of life for up to three billion years. As we will see below, timing is everything in our hunt for aliens.

Over recent years we have successfully placed scientific satellites in orbit around the planet Mars as well as dispatching robot rovers on Mars's surface. One of these robots, NASA's Curiosity Rover, regularly 'sniffs' the Martian atmosphere around itself and in June 2013, it detected a short jump in the detection of **methane**. Recently, this unusual observation was confirmed by ESA's Mars Express in orbit. So, there is definitely methane on Mars; but why is this important and how did it get there?

On Earth, the vast majority of methane is produced by the flatulence of livestock, microorganisms decomposing animal waste and the use of fossil fuels (such as energy generation and transportation). It is the second most important greenhouse gas after carbon dioxide. It does not last long in the Earth's atmosphere (about twelve years), but it is calculated to warm our planet thirty times more effectively than CO_2.

So, the detection of methane on Mars could be a signature of life. Like on Earth, recent research has shown that methane does not last very long in the Martian atmosphere (possibly as short as several months), thus it is likely to have been released very recently. However, there is still much work to do to be absolutely certain. The gas could have been created by Martian microbes in the past, trapped in ice for a significant period of time and then suddenly released when the ice melted. On the other hand, there could be purely chemical processes at work that created methane due to a reaction between hot water and certain Martian rocks. So, we do not know as yet if Martian methane is biological or geological (or a mixture of both) in origin.

We will be very optimistic here and assume that if a planet is potentially habitable, life will somehow always occur 100% of the time or rather $f_L = 1$.

Figure 8: The ESA Mars Express.

The next two ingredients in the Drake Equation focus on whether the alien life forms have developed to such an extent that their presence could be detected. The fraction of planets with not just life but some form of *intelligent* life is taken into account in parameter f_i. Describing what 'intelligent' means here is actually quite difficult. What would any definition of intelligence mean for living things on planet Earth? What yardstick would we use to rank plants or insects against reptiles or mammals? There are a number of possible ways to approach this.

One way could be to consider how long the species has survived on the exoplanet. Land plants have covered the Earth's surface longer than any multi-cellular animal, they reproduce via seeds very efficiently and can exist in the harshest of environments (cacti in the desert for example). Are plants intelligent? If you met an alien, such as Groot from *Guardians of the Galaxy*, you might rightly think so!

On the other hand, it could be argued that the use of tools to manipulate and change the habitat around the lifeform would be important. This shows an understanding of how their environment can be altered to benefit their existence. On Earth, there is much evidence that chimpanzees developed tools (like a stone hammer or twigs for fishing) long before humans. Birds of the crow family have repeatedly shown incredible skills when using sticks to pick out insects from tree bark. Even octopuses have been seen using coconut shells as portable armour for protection!

Taking this further, we could look at the need for these alien lifeforms to communicate with one another — a form of language that helps build groups or societies of the creatures living and even working together. Prime examples of this on Earth are dolphins, whose complex sequences of clicks and whistles help them sense out their surroundings as well as communicate with other members of their species. It has been argued that each dolphin could have their own unique, signature whistle.

Figure 9: An octopus using a shell as armour.

Finally, our definition of intelligence could be extended to include asking if aliens are self-aware. Do they ask the question 'what is life all about and why am I here?' Do aliens have the ability to recognise themselves as an individual creature, separate from the environment they live in and different from the other members of their alien species around them? One famous but simple way of examining this has been the use of a mirror. If an animal (like your pet dog for example) sees itself in a mirror, does it realise that it is a reflection of itself or does it think the reflection is another member of its own species? Dogs have not passed this test yet, though several animals have (including chimpanzees, orangutans, elephants and dolphins). However, human children also tend to fail this test until they are nearly two years old, so we have nothing to be smug about!

There are arguments that over hundreds of millions of years, life would always evolve to become intelligent by at least some of the definitions outlined above. Again, let's be generous and say that f_i is equal to 1 (intelligent life will occur 100 per cent of the time).

Not only does one need intelligent life, but that life has to be mature enough to have succeeded in developing technology and a desire to communicate with other worlds — this is parameter fc. Again, the only data we have here is in reference to our home planet. As mentioned earlier, Earth has been shouting 'I'm here!' for nearly a century now. Unlike some of our superhero stories, let's assume that all these intelligent civilisations are civil, peace-loving and want to simply have a nice little chat with us. Therefore, $fc = 1.0$.

WE'RE DOOMED I TELL YOU!

So we come to our final ingredient **L**, which is defined as the average number of years that a technologically advanced civilisation will actually last. Essentially this is asking how long it would be before an alien culture would either destroy itself (in a nuclear war say) or disappear by another means (for example, some devastating global health epidemic or experiencing an asteroid strike). You need only think of Superman's home planet of Krypton on the point of destruction from the over-mining of its inner core. His escape from the dying planet was the reason he landed on Earth in the first place! But however depressing the thought behind parameter **L** is, it is certainly something that we cannot ignore.

In 1947, the Bulletin of Atomic Scientists highlighted the importance of humankind understanding the perils

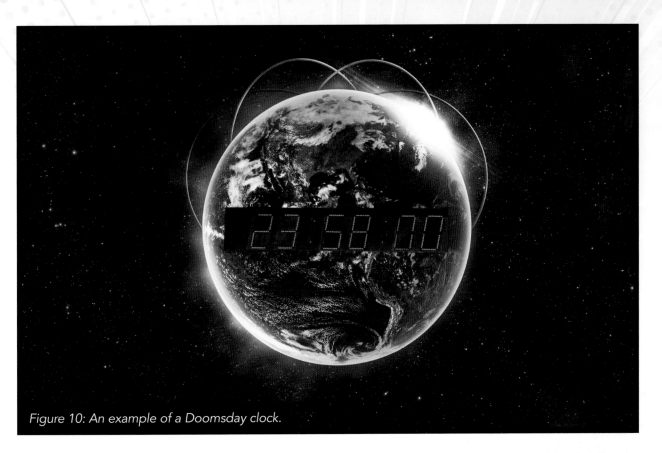

Figure 10: An example of a Doomsday clock.

of global catastrophe by introducing the **Doomsday Clock**. It is a symbol of a simple clock face where midnight dramatically signals the end of the world. Originally set to seven minutes to midnight, the main focus in the late forties was the introduction and use of nuclear weapons. Now the factors influencing the Doomsday Clock time includes the real risk of climate change, such that in 2018, the clock time was set worryingly at two minutes to midnight.

Of course, the above situation is often what superhero stories are all about! Some of the earliest Superman or Captain Marvel comic book stories addressed the threat of nuclear annihilation. On top of this, superheroes are often battling supervillains threatening planetary destruction or, more recently in the case of Thanos, wanting to wipe out half of all civilisations with a click of their fingers!

Estimates for L range from pessimistic (very short time periods like some of the 'modern' empires on Earth) to the wildly optimistic (if a civilisation is developed enough, it might overcome all possible threats and exist for hundreds of thousands of years). Let's take Drake's quite arbitrary range of estimates here of somewhere between 1,000 and 100 million years and put $L = 100,000$ as a very conservative guess (and as we will see, this has a large impact on our final calculation).

AND THE FINAL SCORE IS . . .

To summarise, we have decided to be very positive in our search for extraterrestrial neighbours in the Milky Way, and we will use:

R = 3 suitable planets forming per year

f_p = 1.0 (all stars will have planets)

N_e = 0.2 (twenty per cent of the planets will be in the habitable zone)

f_L = 1 (100 per cent of the habitable planets will develop life)

f_i = 1 (intelligent life will form 100 per cent of the time)

fc = 1 (the intelligent life wants to and can communicate)

L = 100,000 years (a long period of time and hence a large number)

which when we then multiply together gives the possible number of intelligent civilisations in our Milky Way galaxy as N = 60,000 indicating that our galaxy is teeming with life for us to find. If on the other hand, we use very pessimistic estimates such as:

R = 1.5 suitable planets are formed per year (the lower range of the estimate)

f_p = 1.0 (all stars will have planets seems well-evidenced)

N_e = 0.1 (only about ten per cent of stars have planets in the habitable zone)

f_L = 0.1 (ten per cent of the possible habitable planets can actually support life)

f_i = 0.0000000002 (intelligent life will rarely form)

fc = 0.5 (only half of the intelligent life wants to or can communicate)

L = 1000 years (intelligent life is quickly wiped out)

This roughly approximates to N = 0.0000000015 or $N = 1.5 \times 10^{-9}$ which is a vanishingly small number, suggesting that we could be alone in our part of the universe.

This is where the timings for the evolution of intelligent life are important in our extraterrestrial search. If we consider the entire period of time since the approximate formation of Earth (about four and a half billion years ago) up to right now as being just one day (twenty-four hours) then humankind would only appear about seventy seconds before midnight! So there has been an incredibly small window of time when humans have been around and even shorter time for sending out radio communication (as we saw, just over one hundred years). Now bring this understanding to the search for extraterrestrial life. Aliens could be out there, but it could still take millions of years for them to gain intelligence and communicate, or they could have already evolved and are now long dead!

So, there are huge differences in our current estimates of **N**, which shows how difficult it is to even begin to judge whether aliens are on exoplanets waiting to be found. However, in some respects, the actual value of **N** is not important in itself. Whether there are Kryptonians like Superman, talking raccoons such as Rocket or more worryingly, shape-shifting Skull invaders on other worlds, what is significant here is the process of thinking about what would need to occur for intelligent life to flourish somewhere 'out there'.

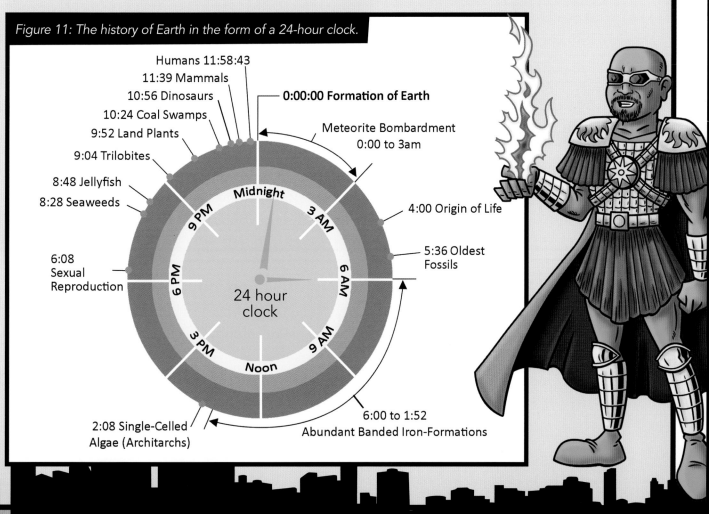

Figure 11: The history of Earth in the form of a 24-hour clock.

Humans 11:58:43
11:39 Mammals
10:56 Dinosaurs
10:24 Coal Swamps
9:52 Land Plants
9:04 Trilobites
8:48 Jellyfish
8:28 Seaweeds
6:08 Sexual Reproduction
2:08 Single-Celled Algae (Architarchs)

0:00:00 Formation of Earth
Meteorite Bombardment 0:00 to 3am
4:00 Origin of Life
5:36 Oldest Fossils
6:00 to 1:52 Abundant Banded Iron-Formations

Midnight
9 PM
6 PM
3 PM
Noon
9 AM
6 AM
3 AM

24 hour clock

GETTING QUICKLY ROUND THE COSMOS

If extraterrestrial life exists at all on other worlds, there is another challenging physics problem that alien travellers would have to overcome.

Let's assume that Starlord from *Guardians of the Galaxy* is on Planet X around Star A when he receives a recorded distress call from Gamora that he is needed as soon as possible on Planet Y which orbits Star B. The Skrulls have instigated an exoplanet-wide invasion and support is required urgently to thwart these evil invaders. In movies and comics, this planet-hopping is a relatively straightforward affair — a quick take-off, engage the 'space jumping' drive (or some other similar-sounding catchy phrase) and in no time at all, our superheroes are blasting their way across a distant alien landscape.

So why is this a problem and why can't we just catch a space rocket ride between planetary star systems? There are a number of important aspects of the physical laws of the universe to consider here. Some of these we are very familiar with in our daily lives here on Earth, while others seem very strange indeed, especially when one tries to travel mind-blowingly fast. As we shall see, at the start of the twentieth century, a certain scientist called Einstein had a range of crazy ideas that over the decades have proved to be true.

THE SLOW BUT DEADLY ROUTE

When travelling between any two points, we need to consider the distance to be covered and the time over which you want the journey to take; this allows you to calculate the average speed of the journey. Increase the speed, and you will cover the same distance in a shorter period of time or in other words:

Average speed = distance travelled/time taken

If you increase or decrease your speed as you travel along, you begin to accelerate or decelerate accordingly or:

Average acceleration or deceleration = change in speed/ time taken

Throughout history, humankind has endeavoured to travel ever faster between destinations. Figure 13 shows the incredible increase in speed humankind has engineered above and beyond any natural abilities. On land, in the air and now in space, we have managed to accelerate vehicles (and hence ourselves) to mind-boggling **velocities**.

In late 2018, the NASA Parker Solar Probe became the fastest ever man-made object. It was part of a mission to improve our understanding of the Sun and used the gravity of Venus to slingshot a spacecraft into a close orbit around the star. Parker Solar Probe is effectively flying through the Sun's outer atmosphere or **corona**, getting as near as six million kilometres to the surface. This is ten times closer than our solar system's closest planet to the Sun, Mercury (with a mean distance of about sixty million kilometres). At its closest approach, the Parker Solar Probe whipped around the Sun at approximately 700,000 kilometres per hour!

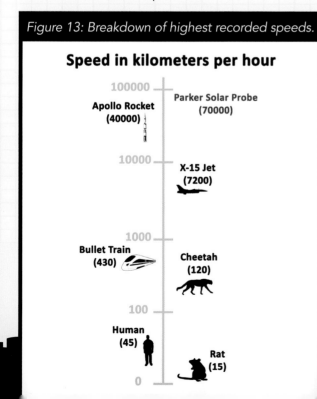

Figure 13: Breakdown of highest recorded speeds.

Speed in kilometers per hour

Those speeds sound encouraging when it comes to potential interplanetary travel. However, even at Solar Probe velocities, we need to get our minds around the vast distances between planets in a star system, let alone from one star to another. For simplicity here, let's assume the planets are at their closest point in their orbits. Therefore, the distance from Earth to Jupiter is approximately 588 million kilometres; at Parker Solar Probe speeds, humans could make that journey in about thirty-five days. If we wanted to reach the outermost planet (Uranus at a distance of about three billion kilometres from the Sun), that could take about 155 days. We are not taking into account the time it would take to stop a spacecraft travelling at such speeds and then place the vehicle into a stable orbit around the destination planet. Aspects of solar system planet exploration are very doable. However, if we wanted to visit our next nearest star (Proxima Centauri) then this is around forty trillion kilometres away and, at Parker Solar Probe speeds, this would take nearly 6,700 years!

Of course, we could try to significantly increase our speed even further and hence reduce the journey time. Any increase in speed requires an increase in energy to reach and sustain that velocity. But, as Einstein proposed and since has been proven correct, there is a maximum velocity that any object can reach — that is, the speed of light itself.

EINSTEIN HAS A LOT TO ANSWER FOR

Albert Einstein published two research papers that revolutionised modern physics, introducing the concepts of **special** and **general relativity**. In particular, Einstein put forward the notion that the speed of light in a vacuum (usually represented by the letter *c*) was fixed. Using laser experiments, we now have an amazing accurate value for this universal constant and it has been measured as 299,792,458 metres per second or 1,079,252,849 kilometres per hour. This is true irrespective of the speed of the observer themselves.

Let's examine the consequences of this. Suppose Groot is in a spaceship travelling at three-quarters of the speed of light (or 0.75*c*) in one direction. Rocket Raccoon is in another spaceship also travelling at 0.75*c* but is approaching Groot from the opposite direction. Now, normally we would deduce that their total relative velocity (the speed that each will observe the other to be travelling at) would be the addition of these speeds; in other words, 1.5*c*. However, according to Einstein's equations of special relativity, Groot and Rocket will see light from each other's ship coming towards them at just under the value of *c* itself. What is happening here?

If *c* (a speed) is constant, then from our basic equation, time and distance must be relative to each observer. So as Groot or Rocket see light arriving at a constant velocity, irrespective of how fast they are travelling

ALBERT EINSTEIN

themselves, then they must be measuring time differently. Or to put it another way, **as they travel faster, time must slow down**.

Also, the property of observed distance must also be different for each of them; **the faster they travel, the shorter any given distance becomes**. If Drax was in a nearby stationary space ship watching his fellow Guardians, then from his perspective, a metre-long space rifle on Groot's ship will appear to be about two-thirds of that size at these speeds.

Finally, as our Guardians travel closer to the speed of light, the more mass they gain, hence more energy is needed to continue travelling at these speeds. In fact, if they approach very close to the speed of light itself, Groot and Rocket will have infinite mass and require infinite amounts of energy to keep going. Only objects that have no mass, such as light, can travel at the speed of light.

Of course, this has profound consequences on our star travelling abilities. Time runs at different rates for different observers travelling at different speeds. Calculations from special relativity show that at twenty-five per cent of the speed of light, the effect is a three per cent slowing of time. On the other hand, at ninety-nine per cent of the speed of light, time is slowed by a factor of approximately seven, while at 99.999 per cent the factor is 224!

For example, in the comics Captain Marvel has the superpower of light-speed. Suppose Carol Danvers wanted to take a quick fun zoom out into space and does this at 0.99999 times the speed of light. If she left Earth and travelled for what is one hour of her time and then returned to Earth again, 224 hours or just over nine days would have passed on our home planet.

On top of that, during her journey, Captain Marvel would have shrunk to virtually nothing and have near-infinite mass! This is not a great look for anyone!

Though these profound physical laws are hard to grasp, the astounding truths of relativity have been confirmed by, for example, high energy particle experiments at the European Organization for Nuclear Research, also known as **CERN**. This group's primary activity is to provide particle accelerators and other equipment needed for unique high-energy physics research, including the famous Large Hadron Collider. Experiments have demonstrated that particles travelling close to the speed of light actually exist significantly longer and travel much further before decaying away than estimated all due to the effects of relativity.

GETTING US OUT OF – YET INTO – A 'HOLE' LOT OF TROUBLE

So, does it look bleak that we are forever limited to travel within our own planetary system but not to and from the stars? If we cannot feasibly travel at the speed of light, what other options are there? Well, one way could be to bend the laws of physics!

Until Einstein, scientists viewed our existence as three dimensions in space (length, breadth and height) with time as a sort of added extra. However, with relativity, time was now introduced as an integral and flexible dimension — we have the four dimensions of **space-time**. Therefore, can this space-time be distorted? Einstein's theory of relativity showed that mass can do this, and we call this distortion '**gravity**'.

When Spider-Man swings up into the air, the force of gravity pulls him back towards the Earth. But how does Spider-Man's body know that the Earth is there? What force is the Earth exerting on him? The best way to visualise this is to imagine a trampoline (a two-dimensional sheet of flexible material) with a heavy bowling ball placed in the middle. The trampoline around the bowling ball is misshapen or depressed. If you stepped onto the trampoline, you would slide towards the ball. Roll a tennis ball around the edge of the trampoline and it will travel a curved path, spiralling towards the middle. Similarly, space-time is distorted by massive objects, such as Earth, which is affected by the massive distortion on space-time by our Sun as illustrated in Figure 14.

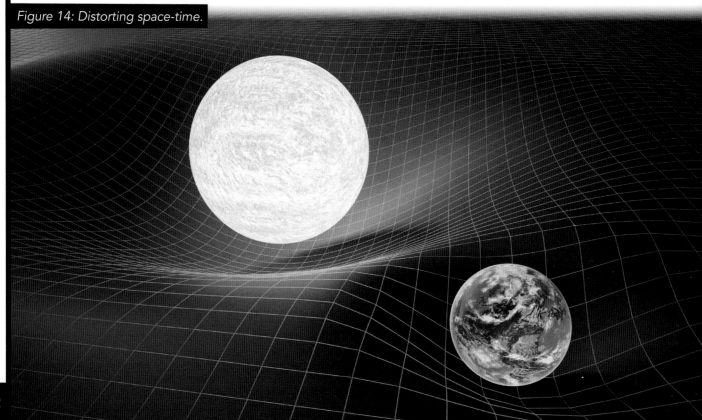

Figure 14: Distorting space-time.

If you increase the mass of the bowling ball, the distortion on the trampoline will be greater. The ball will stretch the sheet more and more, creating a deeper and deeper dip with steeper and steeper curved walls into the depression. But what does this mean for interplanetary travel?

As discussed previously in this chapter, there are many different types of stars observed across the night sky. When a star has used up nearly all its fuel, the way in which it 'dies' depends on how massive it is, with some producing supernova explosions. Then, the centres or cores of these very massive stars collapse in upon themselves. They become so incredibly dense that, if the mass of the core is about three times the mass of our Sun, the pull of gravity overcomes all other forces, creating what is known as a **black hole**. These are not simply regions of empty space — rather they are a seething cauldron that depresses space-time so much that not even light can travel fast enough to escape the black hole's gravitational pull.

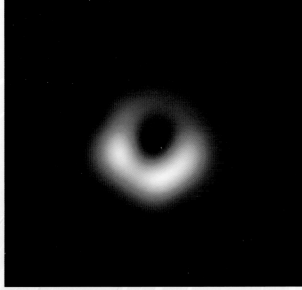

Figure 15: The first-ever image of a black hole revealed in April 2019.

Supermassive black holes are also believed to form at the centres of galaxies and in 2019, an international collaboration of astronomers around the world presented the first-ever direct image of a gargantuan black hole at the heart of galaxy Messier 87. The Event Horizon Telescope (EHT) linked radio telescopes around the world to unveil the first direct visual evidence of a supermassive black hole residing fifty-five million light-years from Earth with a mass six and a half billion times that of the Sun.

So, a black hole stretches space-time to its limit. Now think again of not just one, but two massive bowling bowls on our trampoline, creating deep depressions into the flexible material. Imagine if you could stretch the trampoline material around in on itself so that the two depressions would touch (this is tricky to visualise as we are trying present a three-dimensional problem with a two-dimensional surface but go with it!). The two depressions could theoretically meet, creating a sort of tunnel from one point of the trampoline to another. Instead of travelling the full distance across the trampoline from one bowling ball to the other, you could take a shortcut through the adjoining tunnel. This is the concept of a **wormhole** (Figure 16).

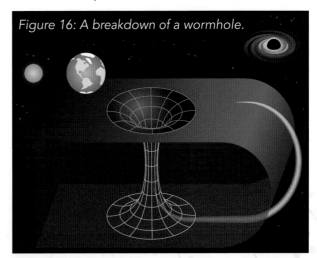

Figure 16: A breakdown of a wormhole.

Unlike black holes, wormholes have yet to be observed, though they appear theoretically possible by Einstein's equations. They have the potential of creating a two-way transportation system across vast distances of space. It is this idea of 'punching through space-time' or travelling through 'hyperspace' that is often the way of getting our superheroes around the galaxy, whether this is Thor's Bifrost Bridge across the Nine Realms, or more specifically for helping a spaceship leap from one place to another in a blink of an eye.

This is obviously a brilliant way of addressing all the problems of light-speed travel. However, there are a number of important issues with wormholes we must consider. Firstly, if we did find a naturally occurring wormhole, we would have no idea whether the other end of the wormhole would conveniently take us to where we want to go! Also, theoretically, wormholes are unstable, with a tunnel only possibly created for an infinitesimally small amount of time before pinching closed again. Then there would be the huge gravitational forces operating, ripping matter into atoms!

In spite of this, some possible workable wormhole solutions have been suggested to solve these issues, but they require the presence of something termed **exotic matter**; this material has the bizarre property of negative mass. This seems unlikely, but may be possible from quantum mechanics. Investigating this further is beyond what we want to outline here, apart from to say that maybe, just maybe, a very technically advanced civilisation could detect, then somehow create enough exotic matter to possibly manufacture a stable wormhole. But there are a lot of 'ifs' and 'maybes' before we get to a position of commonplace wormhole transportation!

CONCLUSION

The popularity of alien heroes zooming across the galaxy, regularly visiting Earth and saving our planet with amazing technology is not going to diminish anytime soon. With about 250 billion stars in the Milky Way galaxy alone and 100 billion galaxies estimated to exist in the observable universe, it may seem that the chances that there is some form of extraterrestrial life in the universe would be high. However, as we discussed here, the conditions required for life to have an opportunity to occur — let alone flourish — can be formidable, to say the least. The physics of interstellar travel is very challenging, but Einstein's genius in proposing space-time and the notions of relativity allows us to speculate that maybe one day humankind will design and build amazing spaceships and stable wormholes so we can travel amongst the stars. Until then, we must be content with dreaming about exoplanetary expeditions through the adventures of our favourite cosmic superheroes.

SUPERHERO MATHEMATICS

SYLVY is a Mathematician working at the University of Central Lancashire, based in the Jeremiah Horrocks Institute for Mathematics, Physics and Astronomy. Her research interests lie in model theory, a part of mathematical logic, including its connections to algebra and number theory. Sylvy is passionate about spreading her love of mathematics to a wider audience. She also enjoys mathematical puzzles, and a variety can be found on her website and on her blog — *Sylvy's Mathsy Blog*.

INTRODUCTION

Through our love of Superheroes, we get the chance to explore an exciting range of mathematics. Some of it is straightforward, and some of it is challenging. Whether you want to shrink to the size of an insect or grow to be a large as a house, let alone try to go back and change the past, some straightforward calculations, equations and thought experiments reveal to us why these superhero antics are not happening all around us all the time!

TURN UP THE VOLUME

A major theme in the science fiction world of superheroes is size: increasing and decreasing. From the very small to the very big, changing size is a trope of the genre. Real-life physics must be ready to take a seat on the sidelines here, because a real animal cannot usually change its size at will. One example that springs to mind is the pufferfish which can instinctively inflate its body to up to three times its original size when it feels threatened. It achieves this by rapidly pumping the surrounding water into its stomach and, of course, this increase in size helps it appear more intimidating to any possible predators.

NAME: Noah Sauvage
ALIAS: Mega-Man
POWER: Changes
        size at will
HEIGHT: Varies
WEIGHT: Varies
EYE COLOUR: Green
HAIR COLOUR: Brown

However, for most animals, all sorts of biological and physical factors get in the way. Suspending disbelief for a moment, some rather interesting phenomena are associated with a change in scale.

Imagine an everyday, ordinary, run of the mill, salt of the earth superhero, whom we shall call Mega-Man. He has the ability to change his size at will: larger or smaller, whatever he likes, something like Ant-Man's abilities. One limitation to this superpower is that he may not increase his height while maintaining his width. In fact, when he changes size, he must keep all his body in proportion. Thus, if he doubles his height, then he must double his width (side to side) and depth (front to back); or if he triples his height, then he must triple his width and depth, and so on.

Firstly, if Mega-Man doubles his height, width and depth, then his volume goes up by a factor of eight. Why? This a bit of simple maths, which we explain with the following picture, Figure 1.

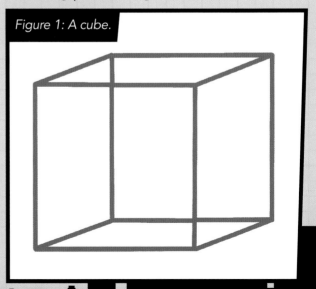

Figure 1: A cube.

Why a cube? To put it simply, it's an approximation to Mega-Man's true shape (which is presumably rather like yours or mine). Later we'll worry about other shapes. So, we suppose that Mega-Man's body is a cube which begins at 1m (i.e. one metre) tall, as well as 1m wide (side to side), and 1m deep (front to back). Thus, his volume begins at $1m^3$ (i.e. one cubic metre). If he doubles his lengths (height, width and depth) to 2m, the volume goes up to

$$8m^3$$

because $8 = 2 \times 2 \times 2$, which is eight times the original volume. You can see this illustrated in Figure 2. Okay, you may have guessed by now that there will be a few formulas in this section.

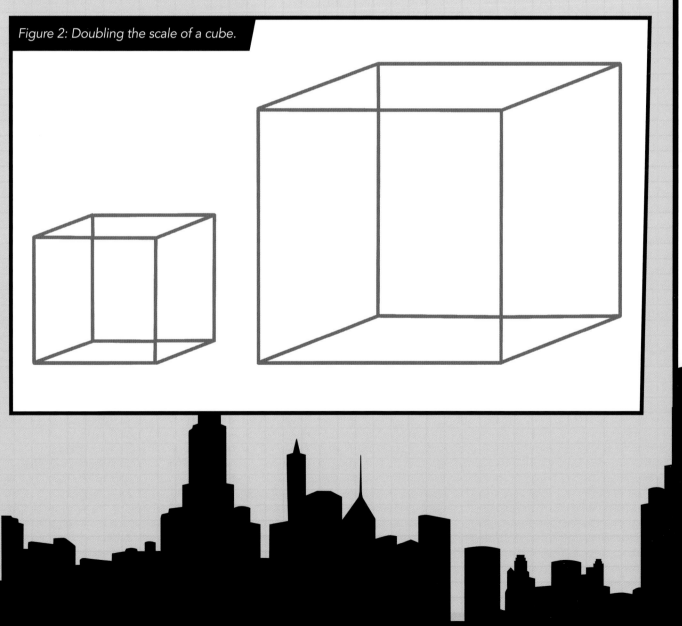

Figure 2: Doubling the scale of a cube.

What happens if we triple the length in each direction? Well, in this case, the volume of the cube becomes

$$27\,\text{m}^3$$

because $27 = 3^3 = 3 \times 3 \times 3$. We can take this one step further. If Mega-Man quadruples his lengths, then his volume becomes

$$64\,\text{m}^3$$

You can see that the volume goes up really rapidly as we increase length.

Something very similar happens in the other direction. Suppose that Mega-Man shrinks by a factor of two, i.e. his lengths (height, width and depth) are multiplied by one half. Then his volume goes down by a factor of eight to:

$$\tfrac{1}{8}\,\text{m}^3$$

because $\tfrac{1}{8} = \tfrac{1}{2} \times \tfrac{1}{2} \times \tfrac{1}{2}$. Likewise, if he reduces his lengths by a factor of ten, then his volume goes down by a factor of one thousand to $\tfrac{1}{1000}\,\text{m}^3$.

There is a mathematical way of saying this: the volume is proportional to the cube of the length; that is the length multiplied by the length multiplied by the length. For short we could write:

$$\text{volume} \propto \text{length}^3.$$

(The symbol '$\propto$' should be read as 'is proportional to'.) In words:

volume is proportional to length cubed.

These formulas mean that if you multiply the lengths by a number X, then you have to multiply the volume by the number X^3.

CONSERVATION OF MASS

So, with all this growing and shrinking, what would happen to Mega-Man's mass? Hang on a moment . . . what on Earth *is* mass? Mass is a measure of the quantity of matter in an object. Mass is measured in kilograms (kg), and the mass of an average human is somewhere around 62kg. An ant has a mass of a little more than one millionth of a kilogram, and the mass of an elephant is about 5,000kg. Thor's Hammer — surprisingly — has a mass of about 20kg. Its weight just becomes infinite when it deems someone unworthy!

Back to the question of Mega-Man's mass. We are constrained by a fundamental scientific principle called **conservation of mass**. In essence, it means that in any physical system the total mass remains constant. Putting it another way, even when Mega-Man gets larger or smaller, his mass doesn't change. **Density** is the ratio of mass to volume: the amount of matter in a given standardised unit volume. As a formula-in-words:

$$\text{density} = \frac{\text{mass}}{\text{volume}}$$

Since mass is measured in kilograms, and volume is measured in cubic metres, density is measured in kilograms per cubic metre. As an example, the density of water is about 997 kg/m^3. The human body is about sixty per cent water, so it's no surprise that the density of a human is just a little bit less than that of water: about 985 kg/m^3. The densest element on Earth is osmium, with a density of around 22,600 kg/m^3.

How does density change when lengths change? According to the principle of conservation of mass, we have:

$$\text{density} \propto \frac{1}{\text{length}^3}.$$

Consequently, a doubling of Mega-Man's lengths results in his density reducing to an eighth of its original value. If Mega-Man decreases his lengths to a third of their original values, then his density increases by a factor of twenty-seven to around 26,600 kg/m^3, rendering him denser than osmium.

There is a problem with our approach by conservation of mass. In the world of superheroes, when the Hulk gets bigger, or Ant-Man gets smaller, they *do* change mass. The Hulk is heavy, and Ant-Man is light (when ant-sized). Clearly, we have to suspend our disbelief and imagine a world in which conservation of mass no longer holds.

We might consider an alternative model to make sense of the change in Mega-Man's physical properties when he exercises his superpower. Maybe in the world of Mega-Man, changing his size doesn't affect his mass; no matter what size he adopts, his mass stays the same. What happens then?

One way to answer this question is to suppose that density remains constant instead of mass. In this case, rearranging the equation for density, we have:

$$\text{mass} = \text{density} \times \text{volume} \propto \text{length}^3$$

Thus, in this model, if the Hulk grew to twice as tall as Bruce Banner, then his mass would increase by a factor of eight.

Remember also that mass is not the same thing as weight. Weight is the gravitational force that one object exerts on another. Usually, we think of one small object (e.g. you!) and one very large object (e.g. the Earth, Moon, or Sun), and we speak of the gravitational field of the larger object, and study how it affects the smaller object — 'the mass'. As another example, think of the gravitational field of the Moon acting on a Moon-walking astronaut, at the Moon's surface; or think of the effect of the Earth's gravitational field on a rocket in orbit around it.

Weight, then, depends on the mass of the smaller object, and on the strength of the gravitational field of the larger object (which in turn depends on that object's mass). As another formula-in-words:

gravitational force = mass × gravitational field strength

The gravitational force is measured in newtons (N), where $1N = 1kgm/s^2$. The Earth's gravitational field at the surface has strength $g = 9.8m/s^2$. For example, at normal size on planet Earth, let's assume that Mega-Man has a mass of 100 kilograms. Then Mega-Man weighs $980N$. However, if Mega-Man were to visit Earth's Moon, where the gravitational field strength g is estimated to be $1.7m/s^2$, which is about seventeen per cent of that on Earth, then Mega-Man's weight reduces to a mere 170 N. If you have ever seen movies of NASA's Apollo astronauts literally skipping across the lunar surface in their large and cumbersome spacesuits, that's because those spacesuits weigh only seventeen per cent of their weight when the astronauts are back on Earth.

What does all this mean for Mega-Man?

The most practical effects come down to his increase in weight. Assuming his density doesn't change, his weight will change in proportion to the cube of his length. So, as he doubles his lengths, he becomes eight times heavier, and so on. That's useful if Mega-Man needs to squash his arch-nemesis!

But how could this be achieved? How might Mega-Man get around the principle of conservation of mass? Albert Einstein had the right idea. He came up with what is likely the most famous equation in the world, namely:

energy = mass × speed of light^2

where energy is measured in joules (J) and the speed of light is $c = 299{,}792{,}458m/s$. In fact, scientists have now switched things around so that a distance of one metre is defined in terms of the speed of light. Seconds are defined by the behaviour of atoms of caesium (a chemical element, with symbol Cs) and metres are defined so that c is 299,792,458 m/s. Nothing can travel faster than the speed of light. So, we get the famous equation:

$$E = mc^2$$

Einstein suggested that at the most basic level, energy and mass are interchangeable. Essentially, they are different forms of the same thing so that under the right conditions, mass can become energy and *vice versa*. So, if Mega-Man does shrink down and needs to get rid of mass and yet remain at the same density, in theory, he could somehow convert the excess mass into energy in the right proportions. Similarly, in order to increase in size and retain the same body density, he could create mass from energy as he grows. However, the amount of energy released on shrinking or needing to be absorbed in growth would be huge. For example, converting 1 gram of mass into pure energy via the above equation gives us:

$$E = mc^2 = 0.001 \times 299{,}792{,}458^{\,2} J \approx 9 \times 10^{13} J$$

That's a lot of energy! As we worked out, if Mega-man shrank to half his size, his volume would reduce to one eighth and he would have to lose seven eights of his mass to keep the same density. If Mega-Man weighs 100kg, the half-sized version should have a mass of 12.5kg. With the above calculation, the energy released by creating this pint-sized superhero would be close to a whopping $8 \times 10^{18} J$, which is approximately equivalent to the entire energy consumption of the United Kingdom for one year!

AREA

But it's not just his volume that is affected. How much skin does Mega-Man have? How much clothing does he require? This is a measurement of surface area, and the surface area of the one-metre cube in Figure 1 is six metres squared (6m^2). In case you've forgotten how to do this, remember that a cube has six faces, and each face is a square with sides of length one metre. See Figure 3 for an illustration of a cube decomposed into a few nets.

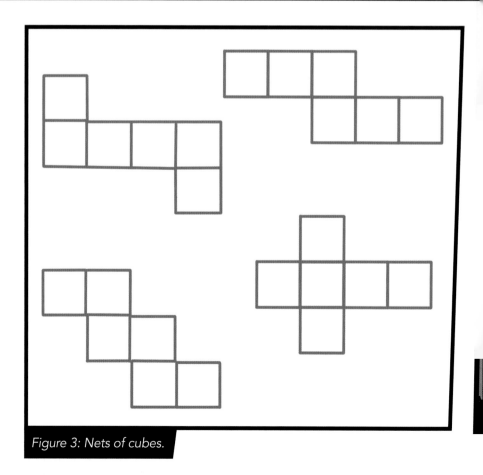

Figure 3: Nets of cubes.

We can calculate how Mega-Man's surface area changes if he changes his size. Suppose first that his lengths double. The area of each face of the cube becomes 2m x 2m = 4m^2. There are still six faces, so the total surface area is 24m^2. That's four times the original. Actually, no matter the scale, the cube has six faces, so let's stop worrying about multiplying by six for now. It's enough to look at how the surface area of a single face varies.

If the lengths triple, then the surface area of each face is 3m x 3m = 9m^2, nine times the original. If the lengths quadruple, instead, then the surface area of each face is 4m x 4m = 16m^2, sixteen times the original. In the other direction, if the lengths halve, then the surface area of each face is ½m x ½m = ¼m^2, one-quarter of the original; and if the lengths quarter, then the surface area is ¼m x ¼m = ⅟₁₆m^2, one-sixteenth of the original.

The pattern is clear: if we multiply the lengths by X then we must multiply the surface area by X^2. On the other hand, we already saw that the volume must be multiplied by X^3. This is known in science as the **square-cubed law**, and it has many important consequences, in nature as well as for our superheroes.

PRESSURE

Suppose that we scale up Mega-Man's lengths by a really, REALLY large number X (say, X is more than 1000). So instead of being 1 metre tall, he is now in excess of 1 kilometre tall. His weight has gone up by a factor of one billion and the surface area of the soles of his feet is 'only' one million times greater. One billion versus one million may seem like an absurd comparison, but this disparity means that the pressure in his legs is one thousand times greater. This is explained by the formula for pressure:

$$\text{pressure} = \frac{\text{force}}{\text{area}}$$

In our context, 'force' is really the force of his weight, gravity's attraction between Mega-Man and the Earth, and we've already seen that weight is proportional to the cube of length. 'Area' is the surface area of the soles of his feet, and this is proportional to the square of the length. Thus:

$$\text{pressure} \propto \frac{\text{length}^3}{\text{length}^2} = \text{length}$$

Ah-ha! So this formula explains that doubling Mega-Man's lengths will double the pressure on the soles of his feet and tripling his lengths will triple it. Since every naturally occurring material has some upper limit on its ability to withstand pressure, this imposes a limit on the scaling-up of Mega-Man.

The observant reader will have noticed that this says nothing at all about non-naturally occurring materials. Perhaps Mega-Man comes from a faraway planet on which people are made from a material unknown on Earth which can withstand infinite pressure. Then he can become bigger and bigger, with no limit. Our imagination knows no bounds.

FLIGHT

In the one hundred and more years since humans developed powered flight, we have imagined ever more sophisticated capabilities for our favourite flying super-humans. Some of them come with wings attached, or jet packs, while others can fly merely by pointing their arms in the right direction and jumping! No matter what the method, there are some physical considerations. It's no accident that birds are usually rather small. So, if we imagine a flying super-human, or a bird, as a machine, what happens to the **power-to-weight ratio** as we change the scale?

Power is generated by the contraction of muscles, which we can approximate as proportional to the cross-sectional surface area of the muscle. On the other hand, weight (the gravitational force) is proportional to the volume. Thus, scaling down will increase the power-to-weight ratio, whereas scaling up will decrease it. For example, if we triple the length scale, we will multiply power by nine (three times three) but multiply the weight by twenty-seven (three times three times three). More symbolically:

$$\text{power–to–weight ratio} \propto \frac{\text{length}^2}{\text{length}^3} = \frac{1}{\text{length}}$$

This little formula explains why it's so much easier for insects to fly than for elephants. In just the same way, it's much easier for smaller superheroes to fly, than for giants. In the Hulkbuster suit that Iron Man uses to fight the Hulk, Tony Stark appears to be just less than twice as tall as usual. As an approximation, that would make him about eight times heavier. The mathematics governing the thrust developed from an engine is — of course — extremely complicated (that's putting it mildly), but as a further approximation, the thrust is roughly proportional to the square of

lengths. Thus, the power-to-weight ratio of the Hulkbuster suit is about half that of the usual Iron Man suit, assuming it uses engines of the same design.

Of course, this is all an approximation to the truth. In reality, the power generated by muscle fibres will not scale exactly as the square of the length, and engines can be re-designed to suit the larger or smaller craft. Also, our approximations presuppose that our insect and giant-size superheroes differ only in their scale. Nevertheless, these rough calculations go some way in explaining why smaller superheroes are sometimes more versatile.

Figure 4: Power and scale.

SUCH A DRAG

When thinking about flight, there is a subtlety we should take care of: namely, drag. This is the force exerted on a flying object by the air through which it passes. It's essentially the same as the feeling of the water pushing back at you while you swim through it. To fully model drag is a major problem of fluid dynamics, but we make another approximation: the force of drag on an object moving through the air is proportional to the square of its speed multiplied by the area of the front of the object.

$$\text{Force of drag} \propto \text{speed}^2 \times \text{frontal surface area}$$

What happens if we double the length-scale of Mega-Man, but keep his speed of flight the same? We already know what happens to the surface area: it will quadruple, and therefore the force of drag will also quadruple. However, this isn't the end of the story: the effect on him of this drag will in fact decrease! This may be surprising at first, but the effect of a force on Mega-Man depends on Mega-Man's *mass*, how much stuff there is in him. If we suppose that Mega-Man's density doesn't change, then doubling his lengths will multiply his mass by eight. Therefore, the effect of the drag will in fact halve! As a formula:

$$\text{effect of drag} = \frac{\text{force of drag}}{\text{mass}} \propto \frac{\text{length}^2}{\text{length}^3} = \frac{1}{\text{length}}$$

This formula explains that when it comes to drag, bigger is better!

OTHER SHAPES

These calculations with cubes have one major drawback: superheroes are not cube-shaped! The idea of approximating real-world objects with cubes, or spheres, or any other straightforward shape, is common in physics. It allows us to simplify the mathematics, but at the cost of accuracy. Iron Man, Hulk, Wonder Woman, and even Mega-Man, are human-shaped, and it's not obvious whether our analysis of the effects of scale on cubes relates at all to the effect of scale on humans.

The reason that we were so focused on cubes earlier is that any shape can be approximated by them. Imagine a sphere packed full of boxes, becoming smaller and smaller. Necessarily, there will be infinitely many boxes within, with arbitrarily small sizes. Nevertheless, we can mathematically analyse the sphere as a 'sum' of infinitely many boxes, i.e. cubes.

This technique, in its full generality, allows similar approaches to be taken with any shape. This is where some more advanced mathematics comes in: **calculus**. Calculus is a branch of mathematics that was developed in the last 350 years or so, precisely to help scientists get a grip on real-world quantities using rigorous mathematics. With calculus, we can make sense of the notion of the volume of a complicated shape like Iron Man; we can work out the shape of Spider-Man's webs; we can find the trajectory of Captain America's shield as it bounces from villain to villain.

Essentially, calculus works by approximating complicated shapes with simpler ones, taking better and better approximations, until we reach an answer.

For example, a circle with radius 1m has area πm^2, where π is the famous mathematical constant, approximately equal to 3.14. Putting a square tightly around the circle, we can calculate the area of that square. Since the radius of the circle is one

metre, the sides of the square are each two metres. Therefore the square's area is $4m^2$. In some sense, this shows that $\pi \leq 4$. By approximating a circle with a square, inside the circle instead of outside, we see that $2 \leq \pi$. Using just these two clumsy approximations of a circle by squares, we have seen that $2 \leq \pi \leq 4$. Using more complicated polygons to approximate a circle, we obtain ever-better approximations to π. The examples of the previous paragraph are not unusual. It turns out — perhaps this is simultaneously amazing and completely obvious — that for the vast majority of shapes we find in everyday life, this approach also works. Using calculus, we can ascribe volumes, areas and lengths, even to relatively complicated objects.

HOW FAST IS FAST?

Some of our favourite superheroes are faster than lightning — so to speak. But Einstein taught us that there is a speed limit to the universe: according to the theory of Special Relativity, nothing with non-zero mass may travel fast than c, which is the speed that lights travels in a vacuum. According to the theory, nothing with non-zero mass may travel faster than the speed of light. In principle, there might be exotic particles that can go faster, but none have been discovered, and the standard model of particle physics does not call for them.

As described above, the value of c is exactly 299,792,458 m/s. However, as soon as there is a speed limit, human ingenuity seeks to break it, and in the world of superheroes it is indeed a common idea. Let's imagine a new hero: Lady Lightning. She can run as fast as she likes, including faster than light.

Let's start her running at the fairly modest end of the spectrum: the speed of lightning. Different parts of the lightning process travel at different speeds, but the return pulse travels at about 10^8 m/s. At this speed she can run right around the earth about two and a half times in one second. I think that's fast by anyone's standards. At that speed, she's already around 400,000 times faster than the cruising speed of a large aeroplane. A large passenger plane weighs about 500 times more than a human being, fully loaded, which means that Lady Lightning's momentum is 800 times greater than a plane's. She can pack quite a punch!

Figure 5: Faster than light.

What about travelling at — or beyond — the speed of light? Well, of course, we must break more than a few physical laws: according to Einstein's Theory of Special Relativity, no particle with any mass may accelerate beyond the speed of light. This includes human beings. But science fiction sometimes needs a little help with the *fiction* part: let's throw the rule book out of the window, and imagine Lady Lightning speeding through the universe faster than light. One very strange effect is that we wouldn't see her coming.

If she is travelling towards us, she will arrive before her own image; and if she stops and turns around, then she will see herself, and be able to watch her own arrival. Time dilation is an even stranger phenomenon associated with moving very fast. It is even consistent with Special Relativity that, if Lady Lightning is streaking towards us exactly at the speed of light, she will experience no time passing. For us, some time would pass, but for her, the journey would be instantaneous.

INTO HIGHER DIMENSIONS

Up-down, left-right, forward-back. These directions describe the three dimensions of space. It's obvious from everyday experience that the space we live in has these three dimensions. As far as we know, space looks like this no matter where you are in the universe (although it's always a good idea to avoid the black holes Rob described in his chapter). Usually, we like to think of time as another dimension, so that's four dimensions in total. Some of the more *avant-garde* theories in physics, namely versions of **string theory** (attempts to model gravitation, electromagnetism, strong nuclear force and weak nuclear force together in one theory), call for

more dimensions, sometimes as many as eleven. Some superheroes have the power to step into other dimensions, and maybe this makes a degree of sense. One way of imagining this is to pretend for a moment that 'colour' is a fifth dimension. 'Colour-space' is then space viewed as the five-dimensional space: three for normal space, one for time, and one for colour. We imagine a superhero called Hue-y, who has the ability to change his colour at will. Hue-y's ability amounts to stepping aside into the fifth dimension.

NAME: Hugh Dyer
ALIAS: Hue-y
POWER: Changes
    colour at will
HEIGHT: 6' 2
WEIGHT: 12st 5lbs
EYE COLOUR: Blue
HAIR COLOUR: Brown

Suppose the world and everyone and everything in it is coloured blue, but only Hue-y has the ability to change his colour at will. Imagine a bullet speeding towards Hue-y, who is tied up, unable to escape. The bullet, and the ropes, and Hue-y, are blue. Using his superpower, he briefly changes himself into red, and the bullet (which is still blue) goes right past him.

The bullet passes right through him, looking only in three-dimensional space, but doesn't hit him because it's completely missed him in colour-space. Having avoided the bullet, he can now walk straight through the ropes and presumably defeat his nemesis, which is the kind of power wielded by Doctor Strange. Although, you may have noticed that, in our example, the floor is still blue, so Hue-y might fall deep down into the Earth.

So, how many dimensions might there be? As mentioned above, some modern physics calls for eleven, but mathematically, there is no reason why there might not be infinitely many.

Seeing into the future, time-travel, telepathy. Each of these is a common superhero trait, found in a variety of science fiction. Many other superheroes have special abilities which give them extra knowledge. Perhaps it's the knowledge of what others know and think, or perhaps it's extra insights from beyond the knowledge of every-day humans.

Some of the more powerful superheroes in fiction have extraordinary knowledge: they know everything, or nearly everything, that has happened and will happen. Perhaps this reminds you of the property of '*omniscience*' — from the Greek for 'all knowledge' — from your RE lessons. But is this possible, even in our wildest imaginings?

In the everyday progression of life, we are essentially time travellers; our lives progress regularly one unit of time at a time. We have also seen in Rob's chapter that if a spaceship accelerates too close to the speed of light, Einstein's theory of General Relativity tells us that for those travelling inside the spaceship, time slows down relative to those outside. This is a form of time travelling into the future as for everyone else outside of the spaceship, time flows faster than for those inside.

Imagine a new character — let's call her Future Girl. She can travel forwards and backwards in time at will. Some obvious problems arise: what happens if she travels forward in time and she lands in the space

occupied (in that future time) by a building. Would she be squished?

Science fiction literature presents several solutions to this. The most common of which is that she can move at will in space and time, together. She can pick where and when she lands. Twinned with this, she somehow knows which spots are safe to land in. In practical terms, this amounts to determining the location of any object at any time, which is quite a superpower.

NAME: Cassandra Pellegrino
ALIAS: Future Girl   EYE COLOUR: Grey
POWER: Time Travel   HAIR COLOUR: Blonde
HEIGHT: 5'3
WEIGHT: 8st 11lbs

The most obvious problem with this kind of time travel is that Future Girl might go back in time and change history. Perhaps she accidentally prevents herself being born. Uh-Oh! Aside from ruining her plans for the weekend, there is a more serious problem: the destruction of time and space itself.

Well, maybe I'm exaggerating a little bit. But something fishy is going on. If she prevents herself being born, then she isn't alive, so isn't around to go back in time and prevent herself from being born . . . and so she IS born, so she is alive, and she does go back in time to prevent herself being born, so she isn't alive and — oh dear oh dear, the cycle continues forever.

This kind of contradictory loop is a paradox, an inherent contradiction. This particular paradox is known as the **grandfather paradox**, since in some especially morbid versions Future Girl accidentally kills her grandfather, thus preventing herself being born, thus . . . no, no, no, we're not going to get stuck into that again!

Figure 6: Grandfather paradox.

What lessons can we learn from this? If we're allowed to suspend our belief in logic, then of course, anything is possible and maybe Future Girl really can go back in time and interfere with history in any way she chooses. On the other hand, maybe logic is the one thing that superheroes can't overcome. Maybe Future Girl can go back in time, but if she tries to change history then something gets in her way. For example, let's say her arch-nemesis steals a vital artefact, which will give him unlimited power, and Future Girl goes back in time to prevent the theft. Let's say that she's right there, about to hide the artefact, but something stops her. Maybe she hides it in the very place that her arch-nemesis first looks! No matter what she does, the events play out just as they were always going to.

This is known as **predestination**: the idea that there are set events that are determined and cannot be changed. Philosophers have spent quite a lot of ink discussing whether this is true or false in the real world, but for our purposes, we're interested in what this idea tells us about Future Girl. Suppose that everything is predestined; although she may go back in time, she may never change history. This relegates her to the status of an observer. She may watch any period of the past or future, but she may not change history, how things were meant to play out.

This hugely reduces the power of time travel, but it's no doubt still a valuable skill.

Finally, for this chapter, let's think about superheroes that have super-knowledge and super-sight. For example, Heimdall from Asgard can see right across space, and Doctor Manhattan, from the Watchmen, can see through time. Such powers should come with a contradiction warning!

Figure 7: Predestination.

Let's turn to one of the most intriguing paradoxes. It goes by many names, but most often it is called the 'surprise examination paradox' and it goes as follows: there is a teacher who sets her students an exam but doesn't tell them on which day of the next week the exam will be, only that it will come as a surprise. They will not know each morning if the exam is to be that day.

The smartest student raises her hand and objects. If the exam is to be on Friday, then the students will awake on Friday morning and will not yet have had the exam. Therefore they will know that it must come on that day, Friday. This would break the rules, and so the teacher cannot choose to set the exam on Friday.

Congratulating the student on her reasoning, the teacher is pleased that another student raises his hand. This time the student says that — since the exam will not be set for Friday — likewise it cannot be set for Thursday, by similar reasoning. Since now that the students know the exam cannot be on Friday, if the exam were set for Thursday then the students would awake on that morning and know the exam must be that day. This contradicts the rules and eliminates Thursday as an option.

By now the other students in the class are catching up. In fact, they argue, the exam cannot be set for any of the days in the next week, and so the teacher must have given them inconsistent rules. She cannot set a surprise examination. The teacher concedes with a wry smile. However, having felt smug all weekend, the students truly are surprised when on Tuesday morning they are faced with an exam paper. 'Surprise!' the teacher says.

What does this paradoxical story tell us? In particular, what does it tell us about all-knowing superheroes? Any superhero that knows the limitations of their own knowledge will be subject to this kind of paradox. Mathematician and logician Kurt Gödel, and others, showed that — roughly speaking — such paradoxes occur in any sufficiently 'self-knowing' system. So there is no hope for a too-clever superhero.

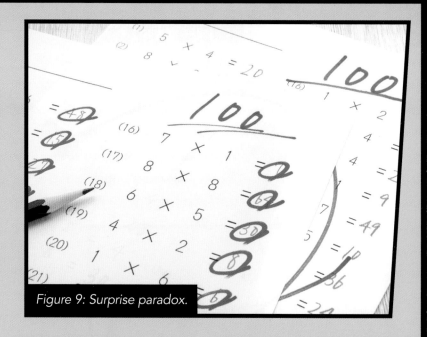

Figure 9: Surprise paradox.

CONCLUSION

We've only scratched the surface of the mathematical aspects of being a superhero, which connects to many different parts of mathematics. Through maths, physics, and even logic, we have explored the powers, abilities and achievements of our favourite superheroes. But nothing — not even maths — can constrain our imagination.

ENGINEERING SUPER-ENHANCEMENTS

MATT is a Senior Lecturer in mechanical engineering. He teaches in areas around concept design and spends a lot of his time taking an idea and seeing if he can make it for real! Matt presents a show called *Comic Book Science* where he takes his vast knowledge of concept engineering to build a working version of superhero equipment, like Iron Man's armour and Dr Octavius' continuum robot arm.

ADAM is a Senior Demonstrator in Forensic Science. He teaches a range of subjects including crime scene examination, forensic testing and analysis. In his spare time, he is an avid reader, loves solving puzzles (the harder the puzzle, the better the challenge!) and designing new puzzles.

INTRODUCTION

Many superheroes use specially designed suits for protection in battle. Batman, Catwoman and Daredevil use relatively simple armour, with no use other than basic protection. Whereas other heroes, like Iron Man, have much more complex suits that respond to commands and can complete amazing tasks. When Tony Stark builds his Iron Man suit, he designs and creates a connection, or 'interface', between man and machine. So how does someone like Tony Stark get armour to respond to the human body?

This chapter will examine how engineering can be used to make technology respond to human signals, and some of the amazing real-world materials that you might see used by Captain America or Spider-Man!

When considering a superhero enhancement, we cannot just simply make some armour, place it upon our bodies and expect to be super-fast or strong. But to understand how these amazing designs work, first, we need to take a look back in time. In the 1600s, Francesco Redi was a famous biologist who was studying the ray fish (the electric eel). He discovered that the eel possesses a special group of muscles that produces electricity called **Hunter's organ** and **Sach's organ**. In the mid-1700s, Redi's work inspired a French scientist named Luigi Galvani to investigate in more detail how muscles work with electricity.

Galvani noticed that the dissected legs of frogs in his laboratory seemed to jump to life in certain situations. When one of his assistants placed a scalpel against the exposed nerve of a dissected frog, which was sitting on a table previously used in **electrostatic experiments** (experiments based on the electric charge created when two surfaces touch and the electrons move from one surface to the other), the legs of the frog suddenly kicked. He continued to conduct experiments, including attaching dead frogs to metal wires and hanging them outside to test the effects of electricity from the atmosphere (lightning) on muscles. Once again, the frog's legs kicked! You can see the experimental set up in Figure 1. Through his experiments, Galvani proved that muscles responded to electricity and also inspired Mary Shelley to write her most famous story, *Frankenstein*.

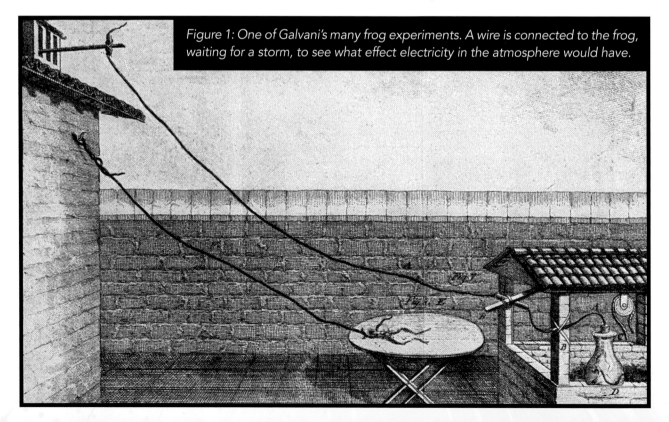

Figure 1: One of Galvani's many frog experiments. A wire is connected to the frog, waiting for a storm, to see what effect electricity in the atmosphere would have.

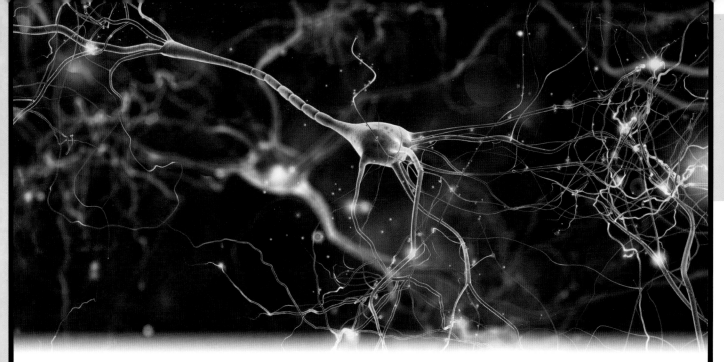

Your body contains millions of nerve cells, called **neurons**, which send messages from one part of your body to another via electrical signals called impulses in order for the human body to move. To create a nerve impulse, your neurons must be excited by stimuli, which could be light, sound, pressure, or reading this book! If you were to stand up right now and try to do a superhero landing pose (please feel free to actually do so!) a multitude of things would happen within your brain all within a single second. Your neurons would help you to see and read this book, then send the message 'do a superhero landing pose' to the brain, and then help the brain decide what pose to do and which parts of your body to move! This **nervous system** is like playing videogames on a computer network, each connected system sending signals backwards and forwards to one another. However, the size of the electrical current produced in these signals is much smaller than you would

use playing videogames or using common household appliances (about 9,000 times less than the amount of current it takes to power your kettle or toaster at home!) But what exactly do we mean when we talk about electrical current?

Imagine there is a water bottle fixed to the wall, and the bottle has a tap at the bottom of it to let water out. If the tap is turned off, it will resist water flow and stop the water from running. But if we turn the tap so it is fully open, water will start to pour out! Depending on how much we open the tap, the water will flow out at a certain speed. So, let's go back to this in electricity terms. The water is like the **charge** of electricity we have, the pressure that builds up behind the tap is like the **voltage** and finally, the amount of water running from the tap — again depending on how much we have opened the tap — is like the **current**.

THE HUMAN SIGNAL

So now that we understand how the brain communicates (with electrical currents), but how we can use them to tell a machine to move through a simple movement of the human body?

In the 1800s, the German physician and physiologist Emil du Bois-Reymond suggested that the electrical activity occurring in the body could be recorded. This process introduced a new scientific area for research known as **electromyography** (EMG), meaning electro (for electricity), myo (from the Greek word meaning muscle) and graphy (the study of). This technique records the electrical activity produced by skeletal muscle by measuring something called **potential difference**. This is the amount of work done moving a charge between two points, divided by the size of the charge. If that sounds a bit tricky, think of potential as 'electrical height'. **High potential** (near the positive charge) is like being at the top of a hill; **low potential** (near the negative charge) is like being at the bottom. Potential difference is the difference in the electrical height between these two points, and the greater the difference, the more likely the charge will move.

Potential difference is measured in something called **volts**. When measuring with EMG,

most voltages are very small, for example, a battery to power a car is a meagre twelve volts. But the voltage found in muscles is almost a thousand times less than that, measured in **millivolts (mV)**. In our previous analogy with the water tank, this would be like opening the tap so small that your eye would struggle to see the flow of water at all!

The range of mV in humans ranges from twenty to thirty mV depending on the size of the muscles of the person. The bigger the muscles (like the ones Cat talked about!) the more electrical potential they have in mV. If you think about a car, the bigger the car, the more engine power you need to move it. If we were to take EMG's of She-Hulk and Hulk, because the Hulk has bigger muscles, his muscles would give larger EMG readings. Not that she wouldn't give him a run for his money in a fight!

In 1929, the German psychiatrist Dr. Hans Berger suggested that the brain may also produce a series of signals like that of the body, but at a different frequency. Through a series of experiments, he was able to record multiple sets of lines, which are what we now

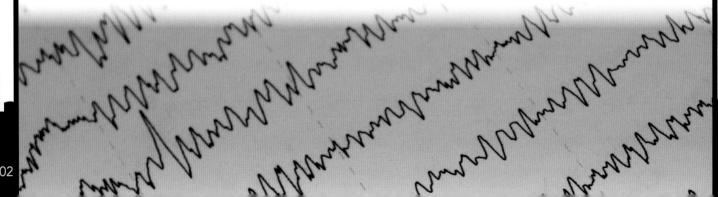

know as **brain waves** (Figure 2). Berger's work had a new and fascinating research area known as an **electroencephalogram (EEG),** meaning to test or record the brain (Figure 2). This electricity can be measured using very sensitive recording tools — **electrodes** — that sit on the outside of the head and detect what is going on inside. Nothing goes into the head; we just measure the electrical activity that comes out of the person's brain. Imagine what the EEG might look like for someone like Professor Xavier from the X-Men!

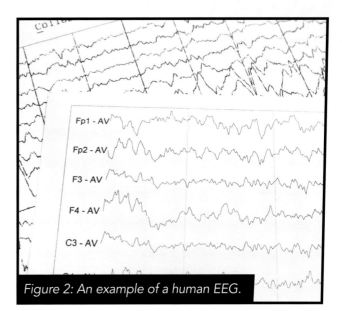

Figure 2: An example of a human EEG.

Now we understand more about electricity in the body and how it can be detected, we can start to think about how we can apply this to control technology like a super suit.

MAKING SENSE OF THE SIGNAL

We can now see that it is possible to speak to the human body and read signals for every action that the body takes. But unless we use some technology to read the **potential difference** from our muscles, we cannot use these signals for any superhero application. One of the best ways to do this is by using an amazing little device called a **differential amplifier**. 'Differential' in electronics means that it has a mechanical function and all its functions are done with the use of electricity. The term 'amplifier' simply means to make a signal bigger. So, when we put these two terms together (differential amplifier) it results in a device that will work when enough voltage is passing through it (Figure 3).

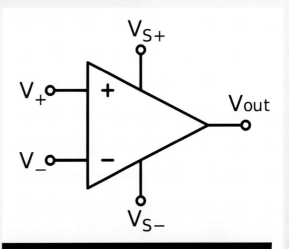

Figure 3: Differential amplifier symbol layout.

The differential amplifier would be used if you had a voltage that kept changing between two different values and you wanted to try and measure the difference between them.

It works by simply taking the positive signal (V_+) and then subtracting the negative signal (V_-). The result is then multiplied by a value increase added to the system called 'gain' (A). Oh my goodness! I hear you cry, what does that even mean? Well, keep it between us — it is dead simple. The easiest way to understand the differential amplifier is to think of it like a bath filling with water. If you were to let it fill all the way to the top, the water would start to flow into the overflow gap (the hole in the top of your bath). The water in the bath is like the positive signal (V_+) and the empty space left for filling the bath is our negative signal (V_-). Then, if we want that bath to fill quickly we can turn the tap to let water gain more flow in the tub, which is what would multiply the difference of V_+ and V_- by to get our output (V_{out}).

If you were to write a breakdown of the output (V_{out}) as an equation it appears as follows:

$$V_{out} = A\,(\,V_{in}^{+} - V_{in}^{-}\,)$$

However, in our search to build superhero tech we also need to use a special configuration of the differential amplifier called a **non-inverted op-amp**. This circuit setup allows us to increase small voltages to a size we can work with. This simple configuration will amplify the difference between two voltages (basically tell us how much water is in our bath by subtracting the water in the tub from the space left) and looks like Figure 4.

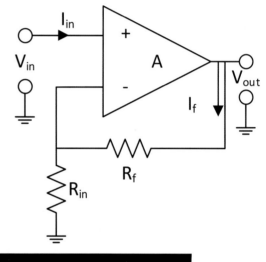

Figure 4: A non-inverted op-amp.

With this circuit we can simply divide the voltage that travels out (V_{out}) by the voltage that travels in (V_{in}), basically giving us a difference that we can work with. A new value (R_{in}) is also added here and it refers to something known as 'ground' or zero volts (0 volts). This is one of two parts used to measure electricity alongside voltage (you will have seen this before when you look at a plug for your TV, it will say twelve or twenty-four volts).

It's important to note that when we say 'ground', we don't mean the ground that you stand on. If we go back to our water in the bath example, when water flows through the drain and down the pipe it will always try to go back to the sea or your local reservoir. Well, 'ground' works exactly the same way. When current flows through the circuit we use it and the rest goes into the 'ground'. This circuit is often written as:

$$A = \frac{V_{out}}{V_{in}} = 1 + \frac{Rf}{Rin}$$

Now we need a way to stick these amplifiers onto our body in order to read the signals from our muscles. You have probably seen the little sticky pads used in hospitals when a doctor is assessing someone. These are called **electrodes** and they are used in all sorts of different ways, with one of the most common ones being the reading of the human heartbeat.

Electrodes can only pick up muscle activity. The human arm has five major muscles which consist of hundreds of fibres that work together to make our body move. This creates a major problem, as this number of fibres packed into one place, all individually moving, means that any signal we get will be noisy. Without inserting the electrode into our body, we also have the problem of natural fat on our arms acting as an insulator and 'muffling' the signal. Engineers fix this problem by placing numerous amplifiers together to try and make the volts easier to read and work with, this is called **smoothing**.

Figure 5 shows the Myo armband, a chain of electrodes designed for this idea of smoothing, however, this does not just take one signal. This little armband has eight EMG Amplifiers placed all the way around the band so multiple muscles are scanned at the same time. This scan is then passed to a little control box and then we can use the signal to do all sorts of things, from controlling our TV through to using super-powered limbs.

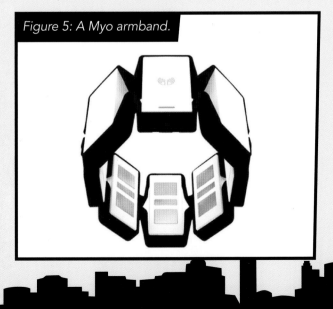

Figure 5: A Myo armband.

We have looked at how we can grab a signal from a human and make sense of it. But this does pose a massive question; all we have seen so far are readings for a single EMG signal, but what happens if you have more than one? Well, the answer to this not that simple. The muscles in our arms have been configured to be as efficient as possible for body movement, but that could cause major problems for scientists trying to read them!

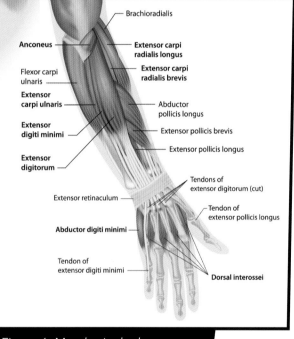

Figure 6: Muscles in the human arm.

Figure 6 shows an anatomic model of muscles within the human arm. On the forearm, there are two large groupings of muscles: one that controls your index and middle finger and one that controls your ring and pinkie finger.

If we wanted to create a super arm like that of Winter Soldier, for example, this proves to be a problem. Research has shown that if we move our index finger and then our

middle finger, the signal produced is very similar; sometimes the difference between them is as small as 0.00001 per cent. To make matters worse, no two people's electrical signals are the same!

When using EMG, we can read one signal without a problem, but when we add further signals this proves to be quite difficult. One way to possibly solve this problem is to use a method called pattern recognition. For example, let's say you're playing a game of Snap. You put a card down, then your opponent will follow, this is repeated until a match is noticed, then the quickest to make the call 'Snap!' is the winner. Recording the voltage in the human arm is a little like this, only far more challenging. Imagine you are still playing Snap, but now you are putting 200 cards down per second and you now have eight decks of cards that you are using all at the same time!

Figure 7 shows what the typical data looks like after twenty seconds of recording. In this graph, there are actually eight different sets of data recorded from around the human arm (hence why you'd be playing with eight decks of cards).

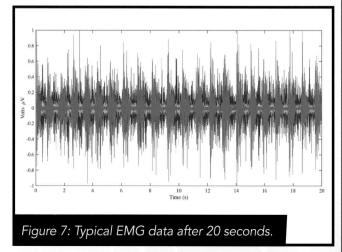

Figure 7: Typical EMG data after 20 seconds.

Now that we know the complex process of moving your arm, how can we start to make sense of it all? There are numerous ways of attempting to convert these complex changes into something useful that we can use in a prosthetic hand; one of the most common is known as **Artificial Neural Networks (ANN)**. These networks use maths to help us understand and replicate brain activity, and this could be used to make a prosthetic hand move.

ANN's attempt to interpret this sensory information (in our case EMG signals) is by grabbing the data and placing it into groups called **clusters**. The patterns that these ANN systems see are always numerical, so if we feed images or sound into them we need to convert the data into numbers so the system can understand it. The great thing for us in our search to make ourselves super robotic arms is the data we want to feed in is already in number format.

So how do they work? Well, let's go back to our game of Snap. When one person puts a card down, within seconds your brain will check many things. First, does your card have the same letter or number on the card as your opponent's? If the answer is YES, you shout 'SNAP!'. If NO, then you can carry on playing the game. This YES or NO matching is useful for computers as they can only understand numbers, so in programming 1 = YES and 2 = NO. This type of pattern is known a **binary** and ANN's love this type of working out. To see how the ANN systems can work, let's turn it into a rule for our game of Snap.

Normally, you are looking for matching cards with the same numbers or letters, so we can change these into our rules:

1. Numbers must be the same.
2. Letters must be the same.
3. Colour must be the same.

So, let's try and put our new rule into a diagram, namely something known as McCulloch Pitts (MCP) neuron.

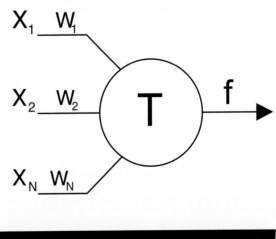

Figure 8: Single McCulloch Pitts (MCP) networks.

So, we have rules, let's apply them to this diagram. We'll say:

- X1 and W1 = 'Are the numbers the same?'
- X2 and W2 = 'Are the letters the same?'
- XN and WN = 'Is the colour the same?'

If all the rules are met, we'll call it T (the threshold), and when we can shout 'SNAP' we'll call it f.

In a deck of cards, we know that half of the deck is red and the other is black. Half of something is fifty per cent or 0.5, so in our rules we can say the rule for colour has a fifty per cent or 0.5 chance of happening. In our second rule, the chances of finding a match are around six per cent or 0.06. So if we add both of our chances together we get fifty-six per cent or 0.56. This is what we call T in Figure 8.

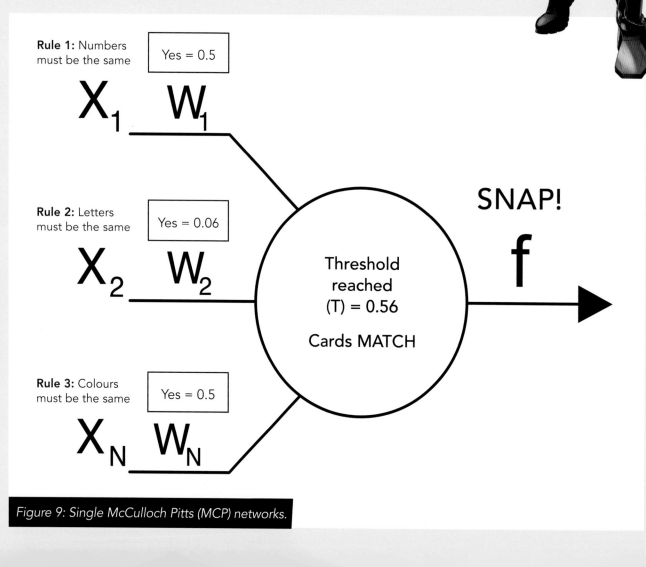

Rule 1: Numbers must be the same

Yes = 0.5

X_1 W_1

Rule 2: Letters must be the same

Yes = 0.06

X_2 W_2

Threshold reached (T) = 0.56

Cards MATCH

SNAP!

f

Rule 3: Colours must be the same

Yes = 0.5

X_N W_N

Figure 9: Single McCulloch Pitts (MCP) networks.

With these rules we have just set up, as well as the ANN, we can get a robot to do pattern recognition for us. The pattern can now make decisions based on our rules that we set (threshold), so if we put lots of these ANN's together they allow us to have a system which will perform pattern checks, allowing us a way to play many games of Snap across lots of card decks at the same time. We can also use it to 'recognise' signal patterns.

When we look at someone like Iron Man, he simply moves his arms and his suit responds accordingly. We now know that one way of being able to do this is using EMG and Tony Stark is using his muscle and mind to control his suit, almost like an extension of his body.

But what goes into designing these incredible extensions to the human body?

MAKING A HAND AS GOOD AS YOURS

We often take our hands for granted, using these extremely sophisticated tools every day without a second thought. Try holding your hands like Spider-Man shooting a web — imagine how many EMG signals are produced to make this hand shape! The human hand has twenty-seven bones in full, eight which are in the wrist, five which are within our palm. It has twenty-nine joints, at least 123 named ligaments and thirty-four muscles . . . it's clear that our hands are an example of complex biological engineering.

Engineering for the body can be seen in something called a **prosthetic** (from the Ancient Greek word prosthesis — meaning 'addition, application and attachment'). This is a man-made device which is used to replace a missing body part due to an accident or injury, disease, or a condition known as a **congenital disorder** where someone is born without a body part. The aim of a prosthetic is to replace and restore the function of the missing body part.

HISTORY

The earliest known prosthetic was a big toe dating back to 1500 BC. It was discovered in the year 2000 on the body of a female mummy in a tomb near Luxor, Egypt. The toe, made of wood and leather, was shaped to fit the woman's foot and attached with straps. The design was so good, that when it was reproduced in 2011, it was found that the toe would allow the wearer to walk barefoot and the toe could even flex! During this time, the use of prosthetics was less of a practical reason and more for a spiritual and religious one. It was believed that the body had to be complete in order for spiritual wellbeing in both this life and the afterlife.

Around the period of the Middle Ages, early engineers like ironmongers and carpenters created artificial hands with multiple intricate systems. Small clamps and pulleys would cause hands to grip, thus allowing a soldier to hold their weapon. A great example of this from history was a prosthesis made for a German Knight called Gotz Von Berlich, as seen below.

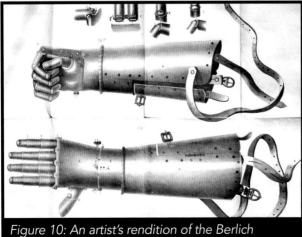

Figure 10: An artist's rendition of the Berlich Mechanical Arm.

The one thing that makes this arm so famous is that it is the earliest record of a mechanical moving arm, based on the man moving his body and the arm moving with the pulleys. Amazingly, the arm was designed with a gearbox so he could make his hand form some basic usable functions like holding playing cards (like our game of Snap!). In the present day, there are hundreds of artificial limbs to be found, from simple hooks that will split and act like a crab's pincer, through to hands which could easily fool you into thinking that they are the real thing.

Now let's take a look at how we can make one of these prosthetics of our own, starting with one of the less complex parts, the finger. We can make skin for a prosthetic finger that *looks* realistic but creating realistic movement is a challenge. Engineers have been restricted by the types of materials we can use to make prosthetic hands strong and useful for many years. Until recently, around five years ago, engineers believed that prosthetic hands must stay in shape, like a robot.

In Figure 11 you can see a prosthetic hand and a regular hand. Look at the fingers, and you can see that the fingers will move like ours, as the joints for movement are all in the exact same place as a human hand. The only problem with these synthetic hands lies in the knuckles, as they cannot spread the fingers. However, this is something that we don't use a lot of, so it is less important than other hand movements. This hand also has had multiple positions programmed into it that are helpful for its user like gripping, pointing or a thumbs up.

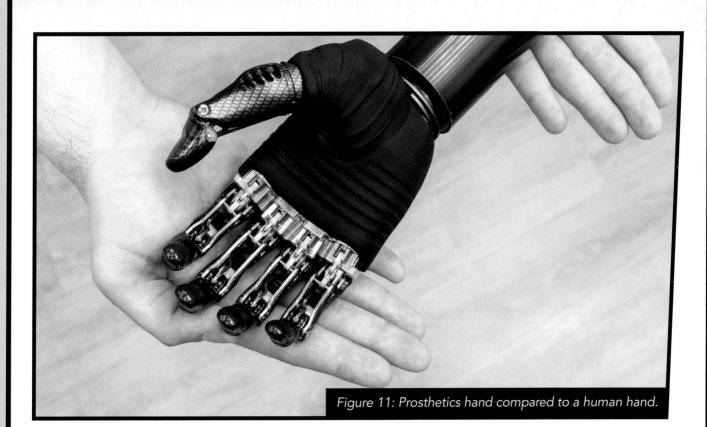

Figure 11: Prosthetics hand compared to a human hand.

In 2016, researchers at the University of Washington created a 3D printed bone hand which can replicate every single position our hand can make and is almost an identical copy to what nature has already perfected: our human hands. This hand is still not ready to be used, but is proof that an arm, like the Winter Soldier's, is definitely possible; we could use some EMG and pattern recognition with some of the amazing new prototype prosthetics that now exist.

So now you know; super suits and mechanical arms that move like real ones are not as far away as you think. But what can we use to make these fantastic creations? Let's look at some of the amazing materials suitable for superheroes!

SUPERHERO MATERIALS

Superheroes often find themselves in the heart of the action, but when the bullets start to fly, they need to ensure they are well-protected. Not everybody can be bulletproof like Superman or outrun bullets like The Flash. So, how do our favourite crime-fighters stay safe? From Captain America's shield to the Batsuit, some form of armour is vital in the fight against crime.

First devised in 1939 by Bob Kane and Bill Finger, the Batsuit — Gotham's iconic symbol of justice — has gone through many changes. Originally designed by Bruce Wayne as a way to hide his identity and frighten criminals, the suit was little more than a jumpsuit, which offered no protection. Through the decades, the suit has been updated to reflect advancing technology. Over the years, the suit has protected Batman against a range of adverse conditions including temperature changes, electricity and fire. However, the protection it offers against bullets is one of the most useful and notable. Could this work in real life? Could you make a suit out of a bulletproof material strong enough to survive a barrage of bullets but be light enough to move around in?

A BRIEF HISTORY OF BODY ARMOUR

From the leather breastplates and chainmail worn by the Celts and Romans to the suits of armour worn by the knights of the Dark Ages, body armour has been around for thousands of years. Whilst these early examples of armour could stop an arrow or protect against a broad sword, they were heavy and bulky and prevented the wearer from moving freely. A knight's suit of armour could weigh up to twenty-five kilograms (the same as twenty-five one litre bottles of water).

With the advent of gunpowder, firearms grew and became more readily available. Due to their relatively low cost, it was easier and cheaper to have small groups of unarmoured men carrying early rifles than a knight in an expensive suit. As a result, armour fell out of favour, with some seeing it as cowardly to wear to battle. However, as weapons became more accurate and powerful, armour was once again required, but it needed to become much tougher, resulting in it becoming even heavier, thus having a direct effect on the wearer. It required a lot of energy to move in this armour, therefore slowing users down. In order to be practical and useful in a fight, something better was needed!

In the 1860s in Korea, one of the first known soft bulletproof vests was invented. The *Myeonje baegab* was worn by Korean soldiers during the battles fought against the United States Navy in 1871. The vest consisted of ten overlapping layers of cotton fabric that was capable of protecting against musket fire.

Figure 12: An artist's rendition of the Myeonje baegab — one of the first examples of soft bulletproof body armour.

After witnessing the ability of a folded handkerchief to stop a bullet in 1881, Dr George E. Goodfellow started to experiment with silk as a possible material for bulletproof vests. In 1887, he wrote an article called the *Impenetrability of Silk to Bullets*. In it, he documented that eighteen to thirty layers of silk could protect the wearer from injury caused by bullet penetration. After the assassination of Chicago's mayor — Carter Harrison Sr — by anarchists in 1893, Polish immigrant and inventor Casimir Zeglen wanted to create a new type of armour that was light enough to be worn on top of, or underneath, clothing. Inspired by Goodfellow's article, Zeglen discovered a way to weave silk so that it could capture bullets fired at it. Working with another Polish inventor called Jan Szczepanik, Zeglen improved his material, and in 1901 the first commercial bulletproof vests were available.

By the 1930s, vests made from bulletproof material had become so easily available that US gangsters started to wear them as protection in shootouts against the police.

Figure 13: Testing bulletproof vests in 1923.

During World War One, the use of body armour was slow to take off, as it was generally too expensive. Due to the size and types of weapons being used, the armour had to be robust, so they were mostly made from steel plates. This resulted in them being clumsy, heavy and unpractical for everyday combat. World War Two saw the use of more lightweight armour with the advent of new alloys (mixtures of metals) and the use of ceramics to enable vests to stop larger bullets. As new materials were invented, the armour became thinner, lighter and more flexible.

In the 1970s a new substance, **Kevlar**, was invented, which would change how body armour was used. Stephanie Kwolek, a research chemist working at the company DuPont, discovered this strong plastic. It is very lightweight, enabling it to be worn comfortably on a daily basis, but still extremely strong, up to five times stronger than steel! Since its invention, Kevlar has saved many lives in its role as body armour. It is also used a lot in sports for protection in the form of padding in clothing and crash helmets.

Figure 14: An example of a Kevlar bulletproof vest.

HOW DOES KEVLAR WORK?

Kevlar, or to give it its scientific name — **poly-para-phenylene-terephthalamide** — is a type of plastic or **polymer**. If we were to be able to shrink like Ant-Man (or Sylvy's Mega-Man!) we could look at the structure inside Kevlar. It is made up of very small building blocks called **atoms**. When atoms join together in groups of two or more, we call them **molecules.** Polymers are very long molecule chains made up of repeating units. These molecules are repeated in straight regular lines, resembling chains. The chains, or polymers, line up next to each other and are tightly bound together with **hydrogen bonds**, making them very hard to pull apart. A chemical bond is a very strong attraction between atoms, due to sharing **electrons** (a tiny negatively charged **subatomic** particle) or electrostatic forces. It is the arrangement of these molecules that gives Kevlar its super strength.

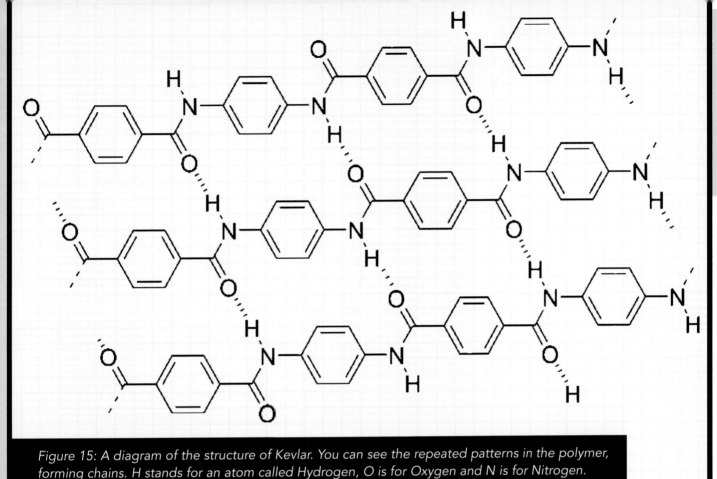

Figure 15: A diagram of the structure of Kevlar. You can see the repeated patterns in the polymer, forming chains. H stands for an atom called Hydrogen, O is for Oxygen and N is for Nitrogen.

When Kevlar is made in the laboratory, it is made into fibres by a process known as **wet spinning**. Concentrated liquid Kevlar is forced through a small sieve-like contraption called a **spinneret**. This results in long, thin, fibres. Think of it like raw pasta dough going through a spaghetti maker! The Kevlar fibres are then wound onto a drum and woven into protective fabric, ready be made into whatever is required.

Now we know a little bit about the structure of Kevlar, we can start to examine how it can stop bullets. In order to understand this, we need to know a little about bullets and energy. Bullets cause damage due to their **kinetic energy**, the energy an object has when in motion. The heavier the object or the faster it is travelling, the more kinetic energy it has.

Bullets come in different sizes, or **calibres**, and are propelled by the amount of gunpowder inside them. Usually, the larger the calibre, the more gunpowder it has, and the more kinetic energy it possesses. Therefore, a bullet travelling from a handgun has less kinetic energy than one from a rifle due to it being smaller. It is like the difference between being hit by a tennis ball and a table tennis ball. Because the table tennis ball is smaller and lighter, it has less kinetic energy, so it will hurt less!

When a bullet hits its target, there is a transfer of energy from the bullet to the target. This energy transfer causes damage to the object it is hitting. An example of this is to throw a stone into a pond. Kinetic energy from the stone is transferred to the water resulting in ripples emanating from the point of impact. The bigger the stone and the faster you throw it, the more kinetic energy it has, and therefore the more ripples it will create in the pond.

Figure 16: Examples of different types of bullet calibre.

Kevlar works by 'absorbing' the kinetic energy of a bullet. As mentioned earlier, Kevlar is made up of tightly packed fibres held together by tiny invisible forces called hydrogen bonds. It takes a lot of energy to separate these fibres. When a bullet hits a Kevlar vest, for example, energy is used to try and separate the fibres. As the bullet loses this energy it slows down and its power decreases. In this way, the Kevlar has 'soaked up' the energy of the bullet. The more layers of Kevlar in the vest, the greater its absorption power. This is why a suit like the Batsuit really could stop bullets!

We have seen how materials used to make super suits have advanced so far. Now, are there any other ways that the super suit could become *more* advanced?

THE FUTURE OF BODY ARMOUR

A recent breakthrough has resulted in engineers and scientists utilising a special fluid in armour development called 'shear thickening fluid' (shear means to cut, like 'shearing sheep'). This is an example of what is known as a **non-Newtonian fluid**. If you were trying to cut a non-Newtonian fluid, it wouldn't get thinner like all other fluids but *thicker*. So, what are these magic fluids and how do they work?

We all know a solid is mass with a definite shape and liquid is mass with an indefinite shape, but a non-Newtonian fluid doesn't follow these rules. If we were to take a pipe and pour tap water down it, the water would flow at a specific rate. But if we poured a non-Newtonian fluid — like tomato sauce — down a pipe, the fluid would move slower the more force is pushing it down the pipe. So this means that if nothing is pushing against it, the fluid acts like a liquid, but when a force acts against it, it will behave like a solid. Ever tried to get tomato sauce from a bottle and shook it hard? This force actually thickens the sauce, so remember to use gentle force!

Coming back to Kevlar, chemists have now developed a non-Newtonian liquid which, when combined with Kevlar, has resulted in what some engineers are calling 'liquid armour'.

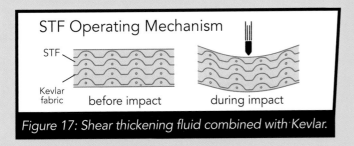

STF Operating Mechanism

STF

Kevlar fabric

before impact   during impact

Figure 17: Shear thickening fluid combined with Kevlar.

Figure 17 shows a drawing of the Kevlar and the non-Newtonian fluid working together to prevent a bullet from piercing the armour. Where armour like that of Black Panther was once something that only existed in comics or movies, deflecting bullets and absorbing kinetic energy, liquid armour could bring this into reality one day soon!

But this isn't the only superhero material that is grounded in real life. Since his creation, Spider-Man has used webbing to climb and swing, so it's no secret; the incredible properties of spider silk have been known for a long time. It is lightweight, flexible and one of the strongest known natural fibres, being five times stronger than steel. Scientists in America have amazingly discovered how to modify the genes of silkworms to make them produce spider silk, enabling the silk to be collected on a large scale. It can then be woven into fabrics, which is used for a range of items from body armour to parachutes. Who knows, in the future, Batman could be asking Spider-Man to help make his armour!

Figure 18: Spider silk — the future of bulletproof vests?

CONCLUSION

Now you know how it is possible for humans to control machines by using technology to read our biological signals — great for superheroes, and even better to create new ways to help those who need to use mechanical limbs. We've discovered some surprising developments in armour, and how the natural world contains some incredible materials that real-life superheroes might use. This is all due to scientists and engineers working on solutions to problems every day, all to make our lives better!

ARTIFICIAL INTELLIGENCE: FRIEND OR FOE?

NICKY is a Principal Lecturer in Computer Science at the University of Central Lancashire. She carries out research into online human behaviour and is particularly concerned with the availability of personal data. Nicky conducts data mining research experiments on social media networks to analyse user attitudes and to discover what impact the data creates. In her spare time, Nicky enjoys charity-based cosplay and cycling on country roads.

INTRODUCTION

This book chapter is about computers; it's also about minds and how the two combine to present what we may call '**artificial intelligence**'. It is also about superheroes and villains, and the idea that one day we may exist in a world where computers have a mind similar to that of humans. In the world of science fiction, of course, that has already happened. With characters such as J.A.R.V.I.S. (Just A Rather Very Intelligent System), the TARDIS (Time And Relative Dimension In Space) and the Star Wars robots (R2D2 being my favourite!), we already have an assortment of artificial intelligence beings to analyse.

So perhaps the best way to begin this chapter is to define what we mean by artificial intelligence. Once we are armed with a sound understanding of our topic, we will be able to examine how superheroes and villains display artificial intelligence (or not).

EARLY DAYS

You'd be forgiven for assuming that AI is relatively new, with the development of computer technology rapidly expanding the world of AI in recent years. However, the seeds of AI were planted long before modern computers existed. This idea actually stems all the way back to Greek myths such as *Pygmalion's Galatea* where a sculptor, scorning human women, carves an ideal wife out of marble. He falls in love with his creation and she magically becomes flesh and blood. The statue, given the name Galatea, then lives happily ever after with Pygmalion.

This idea of humans creating life in their own image was arguably the foundations for AI, and could possibly have influenced one of the central characters of *Doctor Who*, the TARDIS herself. The TARDIS is suggestive, has free will and is self-aware and even takes on a physical form in the episode 'The Doctor's Wife'.

But despite this ancient story, it wasn't until the Second World War that the idea of true AI began to edge closer to reality. British computer scientist Alan Turing was tasked with cracking the **Enigma code**, which was used by the German military for communication, via the use of encrypted messages. It was Alan Turing and his team that created the **Bombe machine** used to decipher Enigma's messages. This created the fundamentals for what is now known as **machine learning.**

But how do we test how much a machine can learn? Or how much it already knows? Enter Alan Turing once again. In 1950, he created the **Turing Test**, with the general

Figure 1: Pygmalion and Galatea.

idea being that if a machine passed this test, then we would be justified in declaring the machine to be intelligent.

Turing wrote an article proposing the idea that a test could be carried out in which a human speaks to two entities, and decides between the two which is human and which is a machine. Turing claimed that if after a set amount of time (let's say five minutes) the human couldn't tell the difference between their conversation with another human and their conversation with a machine, then the machine would have passed the Turing Test and claim to have some aspect of intelligence. In his article, Turing even predicted various doubts regarding his test; issues around philosophy, mathematics and economics which are still discussed today.

In the movie *Blade Runner 2049*, a series of questions distinguish robots known as replicants from womb-born humans. This is referred to as the Voight-Kampff test and is inspired by the real-life Turing Test.

Put simply, it is an advanced form of a lie detector test, checking changes in the eyes and even for invisible changes around the subject's body. Questions are then asked by Blade Runners to test empathetic responses from the individual and judgment is made. But just as Deckard in *Blade Runner* passed the Voight-Kampf (if rumours of him being a replicant are to be believed), chatbots today routinely pass the Turing Test.

In 1980, an American philosopher named Searle claimed that the Turing Test was insufficient in checking for intelligence in machines and he proposed his own version of a test, called the **Chinese Room**. Searle proposed the following test… imagine yourself alone in a room with no one for company but a computer program. This computer program has been designed to be able to decipher and produce Chinese characters (lettering). You do not understand Chinese writing, but using the computer program you are able to translate Chinese symbols that are slipped under the door on a piece of paper. After typing your response, you pass your own piece of paper with Chinese symbols back under the door, fooling those outside into thinking that there is a Chinese speaker in the room.

Of course, the argument here is that it is possible to write a computer program that contains **algorithms** (a set of instructions)

Figure 2: The Chinese Room.

that can make a computer system appear to understand the Chinese symbols, without displaying *real* understanding. Therefore, the Turing Test is now lacking as a test for artificial intelligence. Searle reasons that the Turing Test actually makes it even more evident that computers operate simply by following a set of instructions and cannot possibly comprehend the sense or significance of things. His overall conclusion is that human brains, as biological entities, are organic in nature and evolve from biological processes, and all the most advanced computer can do is mimic them. Nonetheless, there are many critics of this school of thought, and many people still maintain the belief that machines can display independent learning and intelligence. It is worth noting that up to now, no machine has successfully passed the Turing Test in a convincing manner without generating criticism. However, there have been instances when humans who have taken the test have been mistaken for machines!

Critics have stated that the Turing Test is a test to imitate human intelligence and not a way to achieve intelligence. For example, a human will find it problematic to work out big arithmetic problems or calculations, such as $1,786,455 \times 367$ which for a machine is quite straightforward. If a computer is going to pass the Turing Test, it should be mimicking human intelligence, and therefore should be taking a pause and devoting some time to calculate the answer to the question. This is not a way to achieve intelligence, but a way to achieve *human* intelligence. Is it remiss of us to assume that the only type of intelligence is human intelligence? Or should we consider the fact that another form of intelligence may exist?

CAN MACHINES THINK?

So, we can now test for an AI's intelligence, but how exactly does an AI think? We need to view this in terms of human intelligence, the evolution of the human brain, the formation of language and how we communicate with each other.

As human beings, our intelligence has always been one of our most important attributes; it's no secret that we're regarded as the smartest beings in the animal kingdom. But how does one determine intelligence? Scientists have carried out much research in this area and have different views on how we can measure intelligence.

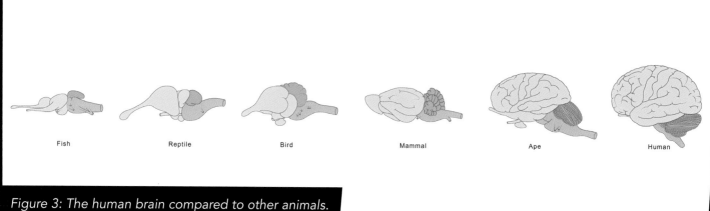

Fish   Reptile   Bird   Mammal   Ape   Human

Figure 3: The human brain compared to other animals.

For example, you may have heard of **IQ testing**, and may even have taken one of these tests yourself. IQ (or Intelligence Quotient) is an attempt to measure intelligence. This means different things to different people, but generally, it means how quick you are at mental comprehensions, such as figuring out maths problems as mentioned previously. **Psychometric testing** is another approach that has existed for over 100 years and is defined by the British Psychological Society as 'an instrument designed to produce a quantitative assessment of some psychological attribute or attributes'. They are basically tools for measuring the mind,

with metric meaning 'measure' and psycho meaning 'mind'.

The field of artificial intelligence attempts not just to understand human intelligence, but also how we can build intelligent entities (much like when we were talking about *Pygmalion's Galatea*). The term 'artificial intelligence' was first used by a computer scientist called John McCarthy in 1955. He explains AI as the science and engineering of making intelligent machines, especially computer programs. He wrote a proposal in 1955 for a conference where he discussed ways of making a machine think like a human, capable of abstract thought, problem-solving and self-improvement.

He is the inventor of the **Lisp programming language**, which has since become the standard AI programming language and remains in use today, paving the way for voice recognition technology including Siri, the iPhone's personal assistant. We could almost think of Tony Stark as being Marvel's very own version of John McCarthy. Stark invents the rather sophisticated and very British sounding J.A.R.V.I.S., an artificial intelligence tasked with looking after Stark's Malibu estate. However, its duties extend far wider than that, and it performs tasks such as providing information when required, carrying out diagnostics and even providing a voice of reason for Stark when his life-decisions, as is often the case, border on the irrational. One could argue that J.A.R.V.I.S. is one of Tony Stark's closest friends, as we see instances when Stark confides in J.A.R.V.I.S. in ways which we don't see him doing with anyone else.

Whilst J.A.R.V.I.S may seem like a concept of the far future, it's interesting to note that a lot of the AI that we are familiar with nowadays began life as a silly idea in a science fiction story. For those of us that remember watching *Knight Rider*, some of the ideas presented may have seemed too far-fetched to become reality.

For those that don't know, the *Knight Rider* TV series followed the adventures of Michael Knight, a modern-day crime-fighter who used a technologically advanced, artificially intelligent automobile named KITT (Knight Industries Three Thousand), that was a high-tech, self-aware, near-indestructible vehicle. Where most of these concepts are still far from reality, one type of technology shown is now very real indeed — self-driving cars.

These vehicles, also known as robot cars or driverless cars, can sense their environment and move with little or no human input. Our current technology means that cars can now virtually drive and park themselves and even be beckoned by a simple command from our mobile phones. They can keep stride with traffic, evade accidents and travel from one destination to another if told what the end point will be. Additionally, a whole world of information is at our fingertips with the integrated voice commands available via Google Android or Amazon Alexa. Cars can talk to other cars, reach out to emergency services, even self-diagnose problems and notify us when it's time to get serviced and repaired!

Coming back to *Knight Rider*, KITT was also equipped with a turbo boost capability that could help the car jump into the air to avoid obstacles. We may not yet have any cars that can fly, but turbo boost functionality is certainly a reality, with electric motors that provide quick bursts of additional power for enhanced performance. We can see this in the active aero wing of the Porsche Panamera (for those of us who may have been lucky enough to have been in one!).

Figure 4: A futuristic concept flying car.

Technology enriched with artificial intelligence surrounds us in our everyday lives. You may have already used your smartphone today, or asked Google/Alexa for some assistance! This constant improvement of AI and its bigger existence in our world is a testament to accomplishments in the field of science and engineering. But to what extent has science helped us in developing AI? Put simply, we can categorise artificial intelligence over time as the following:

- **General AI**
- **Narrow AI**
- **Super AI**

Narrow AI is where we have been, General AI is where we currently are, and Super AI is where we want to go. Well, where some of us want to go at least! General AI can be defined as having all the characteristics in terms of performing tasks that we normally attribute to humans, such as planning, organising, problem-solving, learning new languages and so on. Narrow AI, on the other hand, means that some elements of human intelligence are displayed, but not others. Super AI refers to machines that display human intelligence. Namely, we are talking here about entities that are able to pass the Turing Test without question, without suspicion, and perform exactly as human beings would, without

anyone doubting that they are anything but human. In J.A.R.V.I.S. we see an example of a system that initially began life as a narrow AI but has become a super AI after becoming the human-like Vision.

That's not to say narrow AI isn't smart! The few intelligence tasks exhibited within narrow AI can be completed to a very high standard. In 2011, a computer system developed by IBM called Watson contended on the popular game show *Jeopardy!* to great success. Watson was built as a question and answer computer system capable of answering questions in natural language (communication with no mindful development or planning such as speech or sign language). This was highly unusual for an AI, which is normally created for formal languages such as those used to program computer systems. Watson competed against previous *Jeopardy!* winners Brad Rutter and Ken Jennings, winning the first-place prize of one million dollars.

Similarly, in 1997, chess grandmaster Kasparov was challenged by an AI known as Deep Blue. Up until this point, AIs had been challenging grandmasters but had always lost. But when this computer faced Kasparov at the Equitable Center in New York, that all changed. The atmosphere was tense as the chess grandmaster won the first game, Deep Blue took the next, before drawing the three following games. The team at IBM who had worked on the Deep Blue project had built their machine to compute up to 200 million possible chess positions per second, so it should come as no surprise that the match ended with a ground-breaking win by Deep Blue.

Watson and Deep Blue are examples of **expert computer systems**, but narrow AI. In Deep Blue's case, since its mission was to play chess, it was first programmed with the basic rules of chess, then all the tactics of each grandmaster chess player. Deep Blue then played games of chess with computer and human opponents to apply those rules and build an 'understanding' of how strategies worked. Watson had to answer questions and, as a result, is one of the biggest knowledge repositories ever. Its programmers probably had to prepare Watson for *Jeopardy!* by programming it to find the answer from the question, as competitors must from their own minds.

Advancements in an AI's intelligence are undeniably tied to something known as **Moore's Law**. This was an observation made in 1965 by Gordon Moore, co-founder of Intel. He said that the number of transistors per square inch on integrated circuits had doubled every year since the integrated circuit was invented. Moore predicted that this trend would continue for the foreseeable future. In the ensuing years, the speed reduced slightly, but data density still doubles approximately every eighteen months. But what does this mean to advances in artificial intelligence? Well, to a certain extent, it's more to do with economics than physics. It tells us that each new computer chip will contain twice the number of transistors as its previous version, and therefore it will also contain twice the computational capability for the same cost of production, making concepts like humanoid robots and self-driving cars one step closer to being affordable for the average person on the street.

Moore's Law decrees that certain technological developments are virtually unavoidable. However, there is a consequence to this. Something that may be perceived as ground-breaking today may be superseded in ten years' time. Science fiction is besieged with both superheroes and villains upgrading their human bodies with machinery, but how relevant do those upgrades stay? As an example of this, we can see the 'stark' difference between the Million Dollar Man and Iron Man when we place them next to each other. In the 1970s TV classic *The Six Million Dollar Man*, an astronaut suffers a horrific accident but is rebuilt using technology, gaining a new right arm, new legs, a left eye with a 20:1 zoom lens and infrared capabilities. In contrast, Iron Man's suits are made of super-strong materials reinforced by a force field. Iron Man has superhuman strength, can fly, possesses an advanced laser system, a natural language user interface (F.R.I.D.A.Y), collapsible plating so the user can step in seamlessly, remote control and a self-contained life support system so that it can be submerged in water. The two are most certainly very different, though ahead of their time; but one could argue that the Million Dollar Man now seems outdated and inferior to Iron Man's capabilities.

Today, we can see that Moore's Law has more or less held steady throughout the last five decades. What you might not realise is that Moore's Law only refers to the exponential price-performance improvements of integrated circuits (over the last fifty years) and that exponential growth has been going on for far longer in fields outside of computing, such as communication and genomics (a genome is an organism's complete set of DNA; genomics is the study of this). This is described by Ray Kurzweil's **Law of Accelerating Returns**. In the context of technology, accelerating returns signifies that technology progresses at a speed relative to its value. We are programming computers that will one day program better and faster machines and when the settings for accelerating returns are achieved, we as humans may not understand them, and may not be able to control them. This inability to command the AIs we create is a concept known as **singularity** and it has been explored in various different forms of fiction. Perhaps the most renowned example of AI taking control is in *2001: A Space Odyssey*, the story of HAL 9000 (Heuristically Programmed Algorithmic Computer). HAL 9000 is an artificial intelligence entity aboard a spaceship, when on making an error, must be taken out of service. The supercomputer discovers the project designed to end its life and decides that it needs to eliminate the crew in order to survive.

Murray Shanahan, in *The Technological Singularity,* talks about the possibility of the technological trends most relevant to AI and neurotechnology. He declares that if they maintain their accelerating momentum, precipitating the ability to engineer the stuff of the mind, they can synthesise and manipulate the very machinery of intelligence. He goes on to mention that it is at this very point that intelligence itself, whether artificial or human, would become subject to the law of accelerating returns. It is from this point on that a technological singularity would be but a small leap of faith.

SHOULD ROBOTS HAVE HUMAN RIGHTS?

Whilst there are instances of artificial intelligence that are represented in non-standard forms, the ones that we are most familiar with are through robots. It is this combination of AI and robotics that has caused the most controversy in recent years. Generally, we agree that a robot can function in an assembly line, but there's no consent on whether a robot can ever be intelligent.

Most of us are acquainted with the robots of science fiction without realising that actual robots have existed for centuries. In 1495, at a pageant in Milan, Leonardo da Vinci amazed the audience by unveiling a robotic knight that could sit, stand, lift its visor, and move its arms!

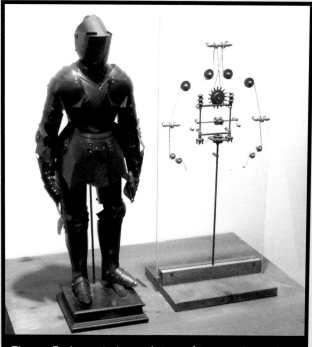

Figure 5: An artist's rendition of Leonardo's robot.

The most popular robots are those that interact socially. A **cobot** or **co-robot** (a contraction of 'collaborative' and 'robots'), is a strong trend in today's robotics developments. They are robots deliberately created to physically interact with humans. This is in contrast with other robots, intended to function independently or with restricted control, which is what most manufacturing robots were until the 2010s.

In the movie *Iron Man*, we see a fantastic sight, that of a metallic hand appearing at Tony Stark's shoulder, just in the exact moment he's given up, holding a life-saving device. 'Good boy,' Stark says feebly as he accepts the device from his robot assistant, Dum-E. The robot had realised that Stark desperately needed to reach the small arc reactor he needs to keep his heart beating, and had made the decision to get it for him. This contact between Dum-E and Stark is an example of collaborative robotics, where robots with cutting-edge AI work with humans, predict our activities and even acknowledge what we need.

One of the most famous and popular cobots in science fiction is R2D2 (Artoo) from Star Wars. Artoo's beeps and chirps are incomprehensible to us as humans, as he speaks a vocalisation of binary called Astromech; something our human brains cannot process. Luke Skywalker uses a translator built into his X-wing to communicate with his metallic companion. So, of all the robots in science fiction, why does R2D2 stand out as a fan favourite? Could it be that the robots in Star Wars act as though they have a wide range of feelings so that it is easier for us to emotionally attach ourselves to them?

The concept of how we perceive robots, and maybe even end up loving them, can be linked to a theory called the **uncanny valley**, a phrase created by robotics professor Masahiro Mori. He explained that as a robot is made to look more human, our emotional response to the robot may become more positive. However, when we reach a point where it appears so human-like that we struggle to tell the difference, we come to think of the robot as creepy and become convulsed by its humanity.

So, what can we learn from this? Could it be that to truly fall in love with robots, they need to be completely indistinguishable from humans?

In the Marvel Universe, there's not much room for this kind of romance, bearing in mind the constant threat around every corner. However, there is a chief exception to this, and that's the relationship between Vision and Scarlet Witch, who is a prime example against the principles of the uncanny valley. In the comics, the witch and the android even have twin boys through magical means! So, if we can take the leap to get to the other side of the uncanny valley, maybe there is hope for love to blossom between humans and robots after all. Or at the very least, we can continue to fall in love (though not romantically) with our favourite non-human robots.

MAKING INTELLIGENT DECISIONS

We discussed the term 'algorithm' earlier in this chapter, and you may have even heard it used before, but what exactly is it and how is it related to AI? It is often said that artificial intelligence revolves around the algorithms used to create it. An intricate algorithm is frequently made up of numerous, simpler ones. This recipe for optimal play at tic-tac-toe is an example of an algorithm:

1. If someone has a 'threat' (that is, two in a row), take the remaining square. Otherwise:
2. If a move 'forks' to create two threats at once, play that move. Otherwise:
3. Take the centre square if it is free. Otherwise:
4. If your opponent has played in a corner, take the opposite corner. Otherwise:
5. Take an empty corner if one exists. Otherwise:
6. Take an empty square.

Algorithm by Pedro Domingos.

Algorithms that are more complex and sophisticated are capable of learning. However, as we have seen in *Avengers: Age of Ultron*, learning can lead to disastrous consequences, namely a potential end to humankind's supremacy of Earth. Ultron's behaviour exposes what some of us fear will be the result of an AI 'gone bad' if it makes decisions that goes against what it was initially programmed to do. But how are these choices made?

AIs often make decisions through the use of **decision trees**. This is a branching method used to demonstrate every single imaginable consequence of a decision. These trees, for example, are used a lot in computer games development in order to programme outcomes into a game. For example, If you were to step into some fire, the game would read that you're now standing in flames and make a decision on what to do next (most likely you'd take some burn damage!). In an AI system, this cycle of *sense*, *think*, *act* would be carried out, with decision trees used in the *think* part of the cycle.

The system would do as follows:

Sense — gather input sensor changes, update state with new values.
Think — poll each decision tree.
Act — execute any changes to actions.

Take a minute to consider how you would tackle an everyday issue that you need to resolve. It might be quite an upfront task such as working out how much money you will have left after buying something. However, it is often the case in life that sometimes we must face far more complicated issues that involve us making a decision with numerous outcomes. We would then weigh in all the factors and choose the best possible outcome based on what solution we wish to achieve.

In this particular case, we would use a decision tree that has biologically evolved in our mind to try and make the best decision. Here is a decision tree that can be used to determine whether we would like to have something to eat (Figure 6).

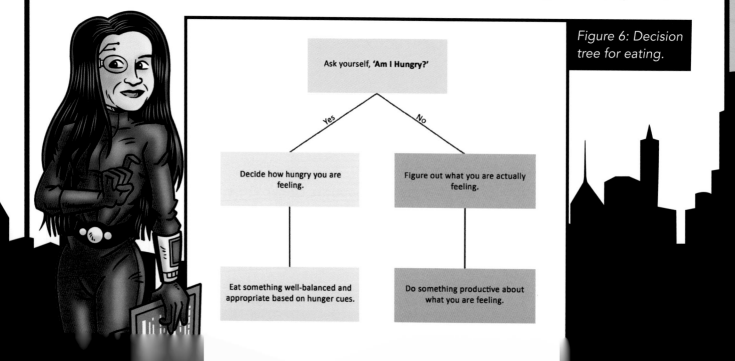

Figure 6: Decision tree for eating.

An AI system will approach a problem in a similar style and must search through the solution space to provide the best result. The solution that is selected in order to yield the best outcome will depend on how that AI has been programmed, and what algorithms and decision trees have been created.

Let's take a hypothetical situation . . .

A school full of children going about their daily activities is about to explode! The people in the school building are unaware of the danger, but our intrepid hero is racing towards the school in an effort to perform a rescue. We can analyse one of the potential decision trees that could be used in this scenario.

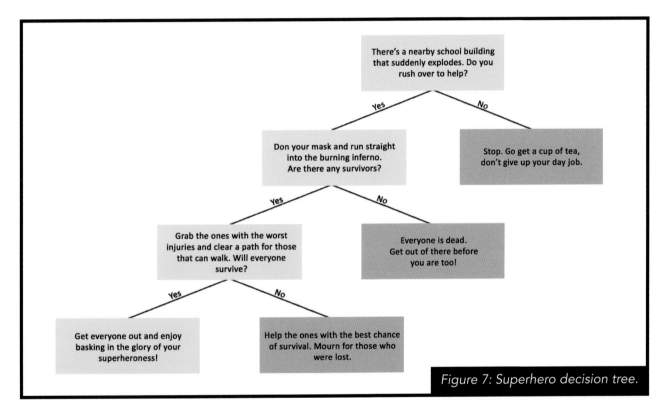

Figure 7: Superhero decision tree.

Decision trees have a natural 'if . . . then . . . else . . .' construction that makes them suitable for aligning them into a programmatic structure. Decision trees are also apt for cataloguing problems where characteristics or qualities are methodically checked to meet certain criteria. For example, a decision tree could be used successfully to assess a make and model of car.

As a result, the decision-making tree is one of the more popular classification algorithms being used in artificial intelligence and machine learning in society today.

People sometimes think that artificial intelligence and machine learning are the same things. You wouldn't be completely wrong to think this, as they are very similar, but there are some differences between the two. As we have already learned, AI is about clever machines that can carry out smart tasks. Machine learning takes that concept a little bit further and is concerned with whether we can give machines data and let them learn things for themselves.

The advancement of neural networks has been instrumental in allowing machines to work things out for themselves. A neural network is a computer moulded after the human brain and nervous system. Professor Marvin Minsky, a scientist whose main body of work was mostly dedicated to the field of artificial intelligence, held the belief that there is no major distinction between humans and machines, and that humans are in essence, machines themselves. He claims that human intelligence arose from the interaction of the various types of semi-autonomous agents that make up the brain. In the future, Minsky asserts, computers will eventually be more intelligent than human beings (although he doesn't state when this will happen, so we can assume he means a long way into the future!). He also warns that we need to show caution to what the future brings, as it may involve an artificial 'superintelligence' taking control of planet Earth and its resources.

This exact scenario has already happened in the Marvel world, when the Supreme Intelligence, also known as the Supremor, tries to take command of the Kree Empire. Supremor was formed more than a million years prior by the Kree to help them create a Cosmic Cube like the one that their enemies, the Skrulls, had created. It is composed of the brains of the greatest Kree minds, removed upon their deaths and assimilated by the super-computer. As time goes by, Supremor gains a mind of its own and declines to make the cube, knowing the dangers it could bring. Notwithstanding, the Kree still admire Supremor and appreciate its wisdom. They are zealously fanatical to it, and even worship it as part of a religion.

Supremor is arguably an example of something known as **The Three Laws of Robotics** (often shortened to **The Three Laws** or known as **Asimov's Laws**). This is a set of rules devised by the science fiction author Isaac Asimov. This means they are imaginary (and also pretty dated) but the notion of unyielding rules that keep disobedient robots in check has stuck around in popular culture.

The Three Laws, quoted as being from the 'Handbook of Robotics, 56th Edition, 2058 A.D.', are:

1. First Law — A robot may not injure a human being or, through inaction, allow a human being to come to harm.
2. Second Law — A robot must obey the orders given it by human beings except where such orders would conflict with the First Law.
3. Third Law — A robot must protect its own existence as long as such protection does not conflict with the First or Second Laws.

Battlestar Galactica's infamous Cylons, who manage to extinguish most of the human race, would certainly contravene Asimov's first law. HAL 9000 would definitely fall foul of the second law, after exterminating most of the humans on his spaceship. In Frank Herbert's Dune, we find that there are no computers, and humans are trained to perform computing tasks. 'Thinking machines' are outlawed, explaining why a movie like Dune, set about 20,000 years from today, has no robots or AI in it. Why? It turns out that in the distant past (from the point of view of Dune, but our distant future), AI enslaved humans and after a battle between suppressed humans and thinking machines, AI in all and any form was banned. It can be argued that Omnius, the almost omniscient machine, was trying to protect its own existence (third law), but in doing so also broke the first and second law.

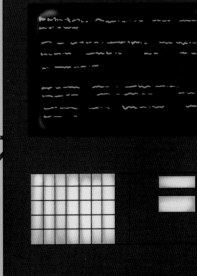

AI IN CYBER SECURITY: HELP OR HINDRANCE?

Going back to our world, criminals are starting to use artificial intelligence for their own evil purposes. In cyberspace, it is common for malware and virus attacks to take place. Hackers can be very skilled and know how to implement tools and techniques that can access secured data, leaving no trace of themselves (known as a digital signature) or what they did. Using AI can allow the defenders to protect against attacks and can safeguard systems against hackers.

Take, for example, image recognition. Nowadays, computer vision is good enough to allow the previously mentioned autonomous cars to drive themselves around our streets. Likewise, image recognition can be used to circumvent occasions where people are asked to solve visual puzzles to prove that they are human. We often see this security measure used on websites, where a CAPTCHA (completely automated public Turing test to tell computers and humans apart) is in place to ensure that only humans can obtain access. At this point, it is worthy to note that CAPTCHAs based on reading text — or other visual-perception tasks — stop visually impaired users from retrieving safeguarded sources. However, these blockades do not have to be visual. Any hard artificial intelligence problem, such as speech recognition, can be used as the basis of a CAPTCHA.

In Marvel's *Age of Ultron*, we see an example of how cybersecurity can go bad. Ultron, a supercomputer that anticipates threats and wards them off before they can reach the planet, is supposed to protect the world. Instead, due to shoddy security, Ultron deduced that humans are a lesser race incapable of living amicably and tries to generate his technological singularity by wiping out human life.

So, how do we ensure that we are ready for AI? As self-appointed gatekeepers of the human race, the consensus seems to be that we don't want robots to take over our world. We need a solid foundation for data before we know that as humans, we can deal effectively with AI and machine learning. Fortunately for our future selves, these dialogues are still occurring.

As we move towards a life full of cleverer and cleverer machines that can learn and think for themselves, we can plan towards a time where machine and humans live in harmony and avoid the terrifying scenarios of enslavement that so many stories have created for us.

ADDITIONAL FACTS

1. One thing that you may have noticed when it comes to the AI that you interact with, like Google Now, Siri, and Alexa, is that the default voice is female. Studies have shown that males and females both prefer the sound of a female voice over a male one. This doesn't just apply to the real world as a female AI is the favourite of Hollywood — with the exception of a few blockbuster movies such as *The Terminator* and *Iron Man*.

2. Artificial Intelligence is able to predict the future. Yes, you read that correctly. Data was fed into an SGI Altix supercomputer, known as Nautilus, from a range of sources. This included the US government-run Open Source Center and BBC Monitoring, both of which scrutinise local media output around the world. News outlets which published online versions were also analysed, as was the New York Times' archive, going back to 1945. In total, more than 100 million articles were gathered, and an analysis of story elements was used to create an interconnected web of 100 trillion relationships. From this data, the computer is able to combine information and create graphs to produce 'predictions'.

3. The smallest robot is called a nanobot. It measures less than ten nanometres in size (or less than one-thousandth of a millimetre). As these microscopic robots are designed to fit into extremely small spaces to perform a function, it is hoped that one day these nanobots can carry out tasks such as be placed in the bloodstream to perform delicate surgical procedures that are too difficult for standard surgery.

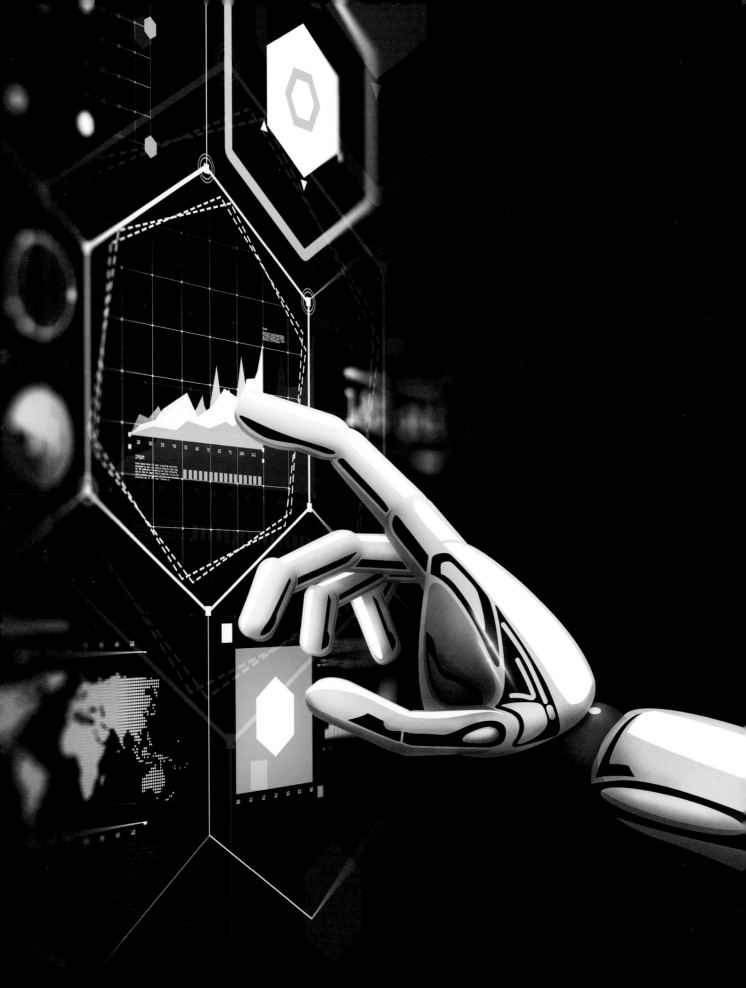

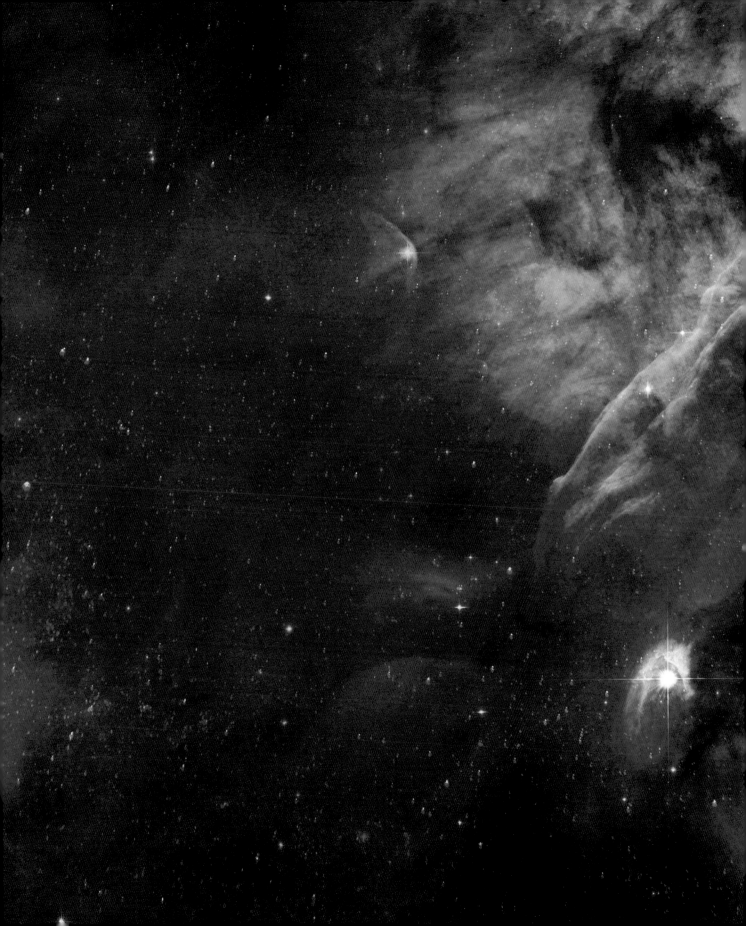

INDEX: SUPERHEROES

ACKNOWLEDGEMENTS, RESOURCES & REFERENCES

Edited by James Phoenix. Illustrations by Daniel Johnson and Dave Windett. Design by Amy Cooper. Special thanks to Hazel Holmes, Imogen Tomlinson and Toni Murtagh.

RESOURCES

If you have any questions or concerns about drugs or anything that you've seen in this book, please don't hesitate to contact Childline through:
Website: https://childline.org.uk/get-support/ Phone number: 0800 1111 Facebook: https://www.facebook.com/childline
This book is not endorsed by or associated with the NSPCC or Childline and this information is provided for the sake of signposting only.
NHS (UK) Exercise guidelines:
https://www.nhs.uk/live-well/exercise/physical-activity-guidelines-children-and-young-people/
FRANK (UK): Information about drugs https://www.talktofrank.com/

IMAGE CREDITS IN ORDER OF APPEARANCE: Key: t=top; b=bottom; l=left; r=right

Adhitama/Shutterstock.com, AnnaliseArt/Pixabay, **Superhuman Bodies:** p8 Everett Historical/Shutterstock.com, p9 Designua/Shutterstock.com, p10 Everyonephoto Studio/Shutterstock.com, p12b 3d_man/Shutterstock.com, p13 Rocksweeper/Shutterstock.com, p14 Maridav/Shutterstock.com, p15 Romariolen/Shutterstock.com, p16 Alila Medical Media/Shutterstock.com, p17 Wysocka Malgorzata/Shutterstock.com, p18 Gentle07/Pixabay, p19 TheDigitalArtist/Pixabay, p21t Designua/Shutterstock.com, p21b anttoniart/Shutterstock.com, p23 OpenClipart-Vectors/Pixabay, mohamed_hassan/Pixabay, mcmurryjulie/Pixabay, p24 Designua/Shutterstock.com, p26l Ody_Stocker/Shutterstock.com, p26r nechaevkon/Shutterstock.com, p27 AlexeiLogvinovich/Shutterstock.com, **Psychology of Superheroes:** p30 Skeeze/Pixabay, p32 rumruay/Shutterstock.com, p34 Sebastian Janicki/Shutterstock.com, p36 Sebastian Kaulitzki/Shutterstock.com, p39 Malchev/Shutterstock.com, p41 MicroOne/Shutterstock.com, p44 aelitta/Shutterstock.com p49 rumruay/Shutterstock.com, **Alien Worlds:** p53 Andrew Barker/Shutterstock, p54 paulista/Shutterstock.com, p56 PaulPaladin/Shutterstock.com, p57 Designua/Shutterstock.com, p58 Jurik Peter/Shutterstock.com, p59 NASA Ames, p65 Aphelleon/Shutterstock.com, p70 Cennet Karaca/Shutterstock.com, p71 FlashMovie/Shutterstock.com, p72 vchal/Shutterstock.com, p73l EHT Collaboration, p73r VectorMine/Shutterstock.com, p75 3000ad/ Shutterstock.com, **Superhero Mathematics:** p82 geralt/Pixabay, p82l OpenClipart-Vectors/Pixabay, p87 Tattoo Worker/Shutterstock.com, p90 jaras72/Shutterstock.com, p94 Monkey Business Images/Shutterstock.com, p95 YourElechka/Shutterstock.com, p96 takasu/Shutterstock.com, p97 Comfreak/Pixabay, **Engineering Super-Enhancement:** p100 Morphart Creation/Shutterstock.com, p101 whitehoune/Shutterstock.com, p102 NomeVisualizzato/Pixabay, p103r Iryna Imago/Shutterstock.com, p103b and p104 Hand Robot/Shutterstock.com, p105 ResearchGate, p106 Alila Medical Media/Shutterstock.com, p110 Wikimedia Commons/Götz-eiserne-hand1.jpg, p113l Metmuseum/Bequest of George C. Stone, 1935, p113r Everett Historical/Shutterstock.com, p114 & p116 Marsan/Shutterstock.com, p117 Angela N Perryman/Shutterstock.com, **Artificial Intelligence:** p120 Metmuseum/Gift of Louis C. Raegner, 1927, p121 Wikimedia Commons/File:2-chinese-room.jpg, p122 Aldona Griskeviciene/Shutterstock.com, p123 GarryKillian/Shutterstock.com, p124 Pavel Chagochkin/Shutterstock.com, p128 Wikimedia Commons/File:Leonardo-Robot3.jpg, p134 Tex vector/Shutterstock.com, p137 Syda Productions/Shutterstock.com

REFERENCES

Asimov, Isaac (1950). "Runaround". I, Robot (The Isaac Asimov Collection ed.). New York City: Doubleday. **Bulletin of Atomic Scientists (2019)** Frequently Asked Questions. Available at: https://thebulletin.org/doomsday-clock/faq/ **Dick, P. (1968)** Do Androids Dream of Electric Sheep? United States: Doubleday. **Domingos, P. (2015)** The Master Algorithm: How the Quest for the Ultimate Learning Machine Will Remake Our World. Basic Books. **Dufour, H. Feuillet, L. Pelletier, J. (2007)** 'Brain of a white-collar worker', The Lancet, Volume 30, Issue 9583, doi: https://doi.org/10.1016/S0140-6736(07)61127-1. **Goodfellow, G. (1887)** 'Notes on the impenetrability of silk to bullets', The Southern California Practitioner. **Kurzweil, R. (1999)** The Age of Spiritual Machines United States: Viking Press. **McCarthy, J. (1955)** 'A Proposal for the Dartmouth Summer Research Project on Artificial Intelligence', Dartmouth Summer Research Project. **Moore, G. (1965)** 'Cramming more components onto integrated circuits', Electronics, Volume 38. **Mori, M. (2012).** 'The uncanny valley', IEEE Robotics and Automation, doi:10.1109/MRA.2012.2192811. **Nietzsche, F. (1889)** Twilight of the Idols. Germany. **Searle, J. (1980)** 'Minds, Brains, and Programs', Behavioural and Brain Sciences. **Shanahan, M. (2015)** The Technological Singularity United States: The MIT Press. **Turing, A. (1950)** 'Computing Machinery and Intelligence'. Mind Volume 49: 433-460. **Wiseman, J. (2011)** The SAS Survival Handbook. Great Britain: Harper Collins.

WWW.UNMASKEDSCIENCE.COM